Exit Velocity

An Entrepreneur's Quest
for Financial Freedom

PATRICK BURKE

Exit Velocity

First Edition
Copyright © 2012 Patrick Burke
Published by Beacon Publishing

ISBN 978-1-937509-27-9

To contact Patrick Burke:
www.burkecpa.com
901 Adams Crossing
Cincinnati, OH 45202
513-455-8200
Business@BurkeCPA.com

Cover design by Ⓢ David Fagin and Shawna Powell
Interior design by Shawna Powell
Author Photo by Helen Adams

Printed in the United States of America.

TABLE OF CONTENTS

EXIT VELOCITY

I hope this book is able to convince you that you don't need to be born an entrepreneur to be an entrepreneur. Although some are called to start a business before they ever work for one, most come to the realization over time that their talents may be better deployed in their own business rather than someone else's. I hope this includes you.

As the managing partner of a CPA firm and a serial entrepreneur on the side (with all the scars to prove it), I have been able to see firsthand not only what makes entrepreneurs tick but also what makes them successful. I have helped entrepreneurs start scores of businesses throughout my career. I am proud that most continue to thrive, primarily because of the drive, creativity, and vision of the founders, but also, in some small part, because I helped them avoid the big mistake.

Many thanks to my clients, all of whom are in some way represented by Tim. Entrepreneurs, although an unruly and challenging bunch, are what make my job fun. I can think of no other position in which you are paid to learn from our economy's highest achievers.

Tim's mentor, Mike, is a combination of several of my business partners, especially my late brother Michael. Michael, thirteen years my senior and the managing partner of a large law firm, was my mentor and the wisest man I ever knew.

Whether you are reading this during your commute (I hope not while driving), behind a textbook you are supposed to be studying, or while at a less than fascinating company meeting, I hope Tim's story provides valuable insight into the challenges as well as the significant rewards of being an entrepreneur.

End your oppression, work for yourself, and achieve exit velocity!

Chapter One

THE DECISION

It was early Friday evening, and Sue Turner was standing at her kitchen island pulling the cork on a nice Napa merlot, when she saw her husband Tim's car pull into the driveway of their eighty-year-old Cincinnati Tudor. She could clearly see not only Tim's exasperation at not being able to pull into the garage because their daughter Kim's Volkswagen Bug was, as usual, blocking the garage door, but also his look of utter exhaustion. In recent years Tim's position as the CFO of Cincinnati General, the city's largest hospital, had gone from his dream job to, in his words, a nightmare of regulation and red tape. As he put it, he felt depressed and oppressed.

As Tim sat in his car gripping the wheel with both hands, his head bowed as if in prayer, Sue thought back just a few years to when Tim was still a manager in health care consulting with a CPA firm. On those Friday nights, although he had worked long, tough weeks, Tim would bound through the front door with a pepperoni pizza for the twins and a gourmet pizza for the two of them. She also recalled they could rarely stay awake past ten o'clock before the combination of a long week and countless piggyback rides or wrestling matches took their toll.

Tim pushed open the door, then walked over and snagged

a glass of wine off the island as he gave Sue a halfhearted hug. Although he was not a wrap-his-arms-around-and-twirl kind of guy, he had to admit his job was making him more distracted and less attentive and affectionate toward Sue and the twins.

"Another week, another 26.2 miles of red tape, and zero improvement in the hospital's financial situation or for that matter patient care. I'd call that the opposite of progress," Tim said with a sarcastic smile. "However, a glass of this merlot should improve my outlook."

After scarfing down a few pieces of Sue's homemade gourmet pizza with artichokes, chicken, and red peppers, Tim retired to the back porch with a half glass of wine and a Macanudo Robusto. No invitations to the rest of the family were forthcoming. Seth, now a twenty-year-old business major home from college for the summer, usually gave his dad a half hour or so before joining him. However, tonight he decided his dad needed company immediately, even though it appeared he wanted some solitude. After taking a seat in one of the overstuffed chairs across the fire pit from his dad, Seth characteristically jumped right into what was on his mind.

"Dad, if you could change any decision you made in your business career, what would it be?"

Seeing Seth looking like a budding young executive in his shirt and tie, his daily uniform since starting at Vision Bank, where he was interning for the summer, Tim realized how important it was for Seth to have a meaningful and successful business career. He also realized that currently his own career was neither.

"Tough question, Seth," Tim said, as he puffed on the Robusto to give himself time to think. "But based upon the level of frustration I encounter daily at the hospital, I'd say taking the controller position there twelve years ago was a wrong turn."

Seth looked at him with a touch of both sympathy and disbelief and said, "Dad, I thought you said the day you were promoted to CFO, five years ago, was the happiest day of your life."

"It's funny—at the time I really thought that was true. Being the CFO of a hospital was my dream job. I thought it would be fun, rewarding, high status, and a path to financial freedom. However, now I don't think it checks any of those boxes. It's allowed us to live in a nice old house on a great street in one of the city's nicest neighborhoods. It's paying for good colleges for you and Kim and for a few nice vacations, but I don't believe I'm fulfilling my potential. I guess as I've gotten older and seen some of my friends with their own businesses being able to see their ideas turn into profitable and valuable enterprises, I question whether that's something I should have done. I guess, in a word, I feel stifled."

"Dad, whether you think so or not, I consider you one of the most successful men I know. You help run one of the city's largest employers and you help heal people every day." Seth stood up, gave his dad a shoulder hug, and added, "Dad, you're only forty-three years old, so it's hardly too late to start over."

Out of the mouths of babes, thought Tim. Seth was right, it really wasn't too late to start over. His cousin Gary had quit his job at a law firm and bought a chain of sub shops. Although it remained to be seen whether that was going to be a successful venture, he'd never seen Gary happier. Gary had said being completely in charge of his success or failure was incredibly liberating. No more unproductive partners or unreasonable clients, just hungry patrons.

Sue looked through the window and saw Tim staring into space with a rather forlorn look on his face, and after getting a debriefing from Seth, decided it was time for a talk. She took Seth's seat and took a sip of Tim's wine before starting in.

"I know your job isn't as rewarding as you'd hoped, but it is meaningful work and at almost $250,000 per year plus world-class health benefits you are well paid. Even the President says we're rich." Tim laughed at Sue's attempt at political humor.

"It's not the money, although that was once the most important thing to me. It's more the feeling I'm not getting anywhere and that I can't make a difference. It seems compliance with rules and regulations trumps advancement and improvement. That's just not me. It's slowly draining the life from me. I am really starting to believe I need to do something different. What do you think?"

Sue knew Tim's reaction was partly a response to what had obviously been a tough week, but what he'd said was still mostly true. "I think you should do what you need to do to be happy. I know you'll continue to be successful in whatever you do. I don't know anyone who has more drive and will to win. You've never sold yourself short before; don't do it now."

Tim and Sue stared at each other. This conversation had been percolating for months, and both looked relieved and happy that they were finally discussing Tim's unhappiness. To break the tension Sue said, "I haven't seen Mike wander over here tonight. His wife's out of town and I know how much he enjoys talking business with you over a cigar and a glass of wine."

Mike Collins was their neighbor, whose spectacular house, although just next door to their rather modest home, occupied a position at the end of the cul-de-sac that afforded it a panoramic view of the Ohio River and downtown Cincinnati. Mike and his wife, Marcia, had moved into the neighborhood just over two years ago to be closer to their son and daughter, who both had families in town. After Tim's father's death five years ago and until he met Mike, he did not have a sounding board for his ideas, or for that matter a sympathetic ear for his business and personal problems. However, more and more Tim sought Mike's counsel on a variety of issues. Mike called himself a recovering CPA and lawyer, which was true; however, in reality he was also a successful entrepreneur, having started, run, and sold two companies and still operating two others. Despite Mike's self-deprecating sense of humor, Tim had found his advice to be unbelievably helpful and his observations uncannily accurate. Mike's only self-congratulatory attribute was his habit of saying, "So I am right again," when Tim would inform him of the accuracy of one of his pronouncements. Tim really enjoyed and valued his "over-the-fence" relationship with Mike and had to admit he missed Mike when he and Marcia moved to West Palm Beach for the winter.

"Sort of par for the course for today—I really have something substantial to discuss with Mike and he doesn't stop by. Maybe the wind's blowing the wrong way and he hasn't caught a whiff of my stogie."

"Maybe you'll see him tomorrow when you cut the grass."

"That's a nice way of pointing out the obvious need for some grounds keeping around here."

Tim awoke early the next morning and, as was his ritual, enjoyed a couple of cups of Zabar's coffee while reading the Saturday *Wall Street Journal*. Being considerate of his neighbors, Tim believed it was not appropriate to start up his mower before nine a.m. and, in reality, he didn't want to risk the ire of his daughter, Kim, who seemingly kept the same hours as the characters in the vampire books she enjoyed so much.

Sure enough, about fifteen minutes into Tim's meticulous mowing of the side yard, Mike's head appeared over the fence. "Your lines are straight, as usual, but you cut vertically last week; you should be cutting horizontally this week to keep your check pattern going," he appropriately pointed out.

"You know what, Mike, you're right. I guess I'm preoccupied."

"I was going to stop over last night; however, when I saw you and Sue on your porch it looked like you were having a pretty serious discussion, so I thought I'd better not interrupt."

"Well, it was pretty serious, but believe it or not, you could have helped."

"Oh really? If any sort of marital advice is needed I always yield to Dr. Phil."

"No, actually it's more like career and business advice that I know you're qualified to give, or so you've been telling me for the last two years," Tim replied.

"OK, now you've got my attention. What seems to be the problem?"

"I'll buy you a lemonade after I finish the lawn and seek your wise counsel."

"Deal, only let's make it a milk shake and a hamburger. Marcia is out of town and I've been craving some high-end junk food."

Later, as they were walking into Aglamesis Brothers, an old-fashioned ice cream parlor, Tim said to Mike, "It's nice of you to take the time to listen to my problems. Either you are truly a good man or bored to tears and really looking for a distraction."

"Probably as much of one as the other, or maybe I'm just a sucker for an old-fashioned milk shake. I love that they give you the steel mixing container with a little extra after you've slurped down your first glass. You know, Tim, that little extra costs so little and makes you feel like you somehow got not only a great shake but also a little bonus. So few experiences today leave you with that feeling."

Mike was sounding wistful. Perhaps it was the black-and-white tile floors and the marble counters that naturally inspire such "old-fashioned" thoughts. It was observations like this that caused Tim to enjoy his talks with Mike so much.

"Tim, since you're buying and my time is valuable, or at least it once was, let's get right to it. What seems to be your problem?"

As the burgers and shakes were served, Tim explained his frustration with his job and his gnawing feeling that there should be more he could do with what he considered his strong skill set.

"I understand your feelings," Mike sympathized. "I remember feeling the same way when I was working at the law firm, before I bought my first company. However, the level of your frustration has actually done you a favor."

"How's that?" asked Tim.

"It's given you exit velocity."

"Exit velocity?"

"I've seen it often; cathartic really. There comes a time when it is obvious that your ambition and drive can't be matched or harnessed by your employer. As a result, your frustration has propelled you to break the strong gravitational pull of a steady job."

"As usual, well put," said Tim. "So long as we're using space metaphors, do you think I have the right stuff to be a successful entrepreneur?"

"You know, we've never worked together, but I'd like to think with all the hiring and, unfortunately, firing I've done I am a pretty good judge of talent. And I'd put you in the top quartile. You're smart and technical, which is pretty common. What is uncommon is your judgment and people skills."

As Tim looked at Mike quizzically, Mike continued. "I've watched you at neighborhood parties. You're always the one asking questions to try to learn more about people, and not in a nosy way. That's a fantastic attribute. Most people at those functions are so busy bragging about their children, job, or golf game, I'd bet they rarely remember who they spoke to, much less anything meaningful about that person. You've probably heard that old Dale Carnegie quote that you can make more friends in two months by becoming interested in other people than you can in two years by trying to get other people interested in you. Fits you to a tee. With respect to your judgment, I think I've gotten a good sense of that watching you interact with Sue and the twins. As a thirty-five-year veteran of marriage, father of three, and grandfather of six, I know maintaining a happy marriage and raising children who are productive members of society is no mean feat."

As usual, Tim was somewhat taken aback, not only by Mike's characteristically blunt assessment but also by his ability to gain meaningful insights from seemingly simple observations.

"Thanks, Mike. I guess I agree with your assessment since it's so positive; however, I was hoping you'd say I was a top-ten-percent kind of guy," Tim said with a grin.

"You could be; I just have never seen you in action with your pinstripes on."

"I like to think you'd be impressed; however, I know successful entrepreneurs are the epitome of a tough crowd."

"Enough of the mutual admiration society—what's so important that you dragged me out here to put my statin medication to the ultimate test?"

"First, one more compliment. I know you're a very successful entrepreneur, and under the rubric of it takes one to know one, do you think I have what it takes to run my own business?"

"How did you get from feeling frustrated with your job to wanting to run your own business?" asked Mike.

"You know, being the CFO of Cincinnati General was my career goal. Even though I'm in what I thought would be my dream position, I don't think I'll ever have the opportunity to make a difference in how effectively the hospital operates. We still deliver world-class care, but there's so much more we could do if we could be more efficient collecting from our private and government payers. And if we didn't practice so much defensive medicine, we could actually innovate. As I get older, I guess the idea of making a difference is becoming more important to me. Instead, I end up spending what could be my how-can-we-improve time dealing with the government, the insurance companies, and responding to what are often meaningless inquiries from board members."

Mike stared at Tim appraisingly and after a long pause said, "Tim, as I am sure you know, as you climb the corporate ladder, each rung has more frustrations, politics, HR issues, and overall amplifications of the human condition. That's why effective public company CEOs are so hard to find and when a company finds a good one they overpay to keep him or her. Of course, running your own business has its own set of issues; however, just the fact that the business is yours and you're maneuvering through this morass for yourself gives you far more tolerance and what I call business stamina. I guess you won't find it hard to believe that I've had this discussion often enough with others that I have some strong opinions on what it takes to be a successful business owner."

Tim laughed and said, "You with a strong opinion? Hard to imagine. At the risk of having my barely germinated seed of an idea ripped unceremoniously from the earth, please continue, but be gentle."

"I'm afraid it's a little too late for me to change my style, so here it comes, both barrels. I believe there are ten questions you have to ask yourself before you decide you're going to be an entrepreneur. The first is, Can you live with uncertainty? I know from our previous discussions your dad's career was typical of a successful businessman whose career started in the 1950s. He stayed

with First Cincinnati Bank for his whole career and probably retired with a nice pension and probably some company stock that
made retirement comfortable for your mother and him. And I'm
sure as a result your mother still has no financial concerns."

Tim said, "You're right. I guess although that scenario is not
something I necessarily sought out, I believed it would be one
of the rewards for a successful career. However, now, honestly,
even if that secure retirement was waiting for me at the hospital,
which it's not, it wouldn't be enough for me to tolerate twenty
more years of this level of frustration."

"It's funny—non-entrepreneurs only see the tangible results
of a successful business, like a nice house, cars, and vacations, but
see nothing of the process. As a business owner your business's
performance and therefore your income can and will be affected
by many factors that are completely out of your control. Interest
rates, lending environment, stock market performance, the labor
market, and even public sentiment, which of late has been particularly hard to predict, all play a part. Do you believe you can live
with that level of uncertainty—and just as important, can Sue?"

"That's a heck of a first question," said Tim. "You know, I've
never examined my conscience on that before, but I believe I
could hack it. I also think Sue could live with it if she knew I was
happier and felt more productive."

"Good, you've run the first trap. Now, on a related topic, how
would you rate your tolerance for real risk? And I don't mean
leaving your umbrella home on a cloudy day. Understand, it's not
just your treasure at risk; it's also your time and talent. All entrepreneurial businesses require a certain amount of wildcatting.

If you're deathly afraid of drilling a dry hole, owning your own business isn't for you. In ~~addition, effort~~ and results don't necessarily have a plus-one correlation. The good news is there is a flip side, and that is when a business is really humming, it often seems effortless. It's like crushing a two-hundred-yard six iron when it feels like you barely swung the club. "

Tim responded, "I don't think I can eat risk for breakfast, and I also don't think it would be on my lunch menu."

Mike laughed. "Colorfully put, but entrepreneurs learn pretty quickly the only way to grow their business and make more money is to assume ever-larger risks. In a way, it's like moving up from the five-dollar table to the no-limit table. You have to have confidence in your ability to suss out the business risk and skew the odds toward yourself."

"Gotcha—what's number three?"

"What's your relationship with your money? If you treat it like a baseball card collection and enjoy taking it out and looking at it and occasionally adding a card here or there, you're probably not an entrepreneur. The value of your business will be very hard to track, so it's hard to track the return on your invested capital. However, if you continue to generate more revenue every year and are able to put a higher percentage of that revenue on the bottom line, you're increasing the value of your business and the money you've invested in it. You know, the most successful entrepreneurs treat money like a renewable resource; they don't worry about investing in their business. They're confident that their investment today will mean more profits tomorrow. It's all about a bigger future."

Tim had to admit this made him a little uncomfortable. "I like to think I don't have an unhealthy attachment to my money," he said. "I'm careful about how we spend and I'm proud of how we've invested and how much our investments have grown. However, I'd have to admit that if I project where we will be based on our current rate of savings, including my retirement plan, it's nowhere close to where I'd like to be."

"It's good you've gone through that exercise. In my experience as an entrepreneur as well as my time as an adviser, I know everyone has a different number, just like that commercial where everyone is lugging around a giant figure. I call that number exit velocity. You know, the amount that propels you into the orbit of complete financial freedom."

"Exit velocity; that's a great way to put it. I have enough trust in my skills and judgment that parting with some of my own money and putting the rest at risk is something I'm willing to do." Tim, warming up, added, "This is really an exciting way to look at business, isn't it?"

"Yeah, it really is kind of a game. It's funny—the most successful entrepreneurs I know are hypercompetitive and are rarely driven by money except to the extent that it's the only scoreboard available.

"OK," Mike continued, "on to number four. Can you lead people? Unless your business is going to be just you, like a shoeshine stand or consulting, you're going to need to lead and motivate people. Fortunately—or unfortunately, depending on your outlook—money isn't the primary motivational tool. To get the most from your employees, they need to know you value them.

You don't need to swap hopes and dreams over a plate of fudge, but you need to be genuinely interested in their aspirations and actively communicate that to them. Businesses that help their employees realize their nonbusiness goals and dreams consistently beat businesses that view and treat employees as productive units only."

"Like a good team captain?"

"Exactly, and a great lead-in for the fifth question: How competitive are you?"

"I always enjoyed sports, particularly basketball. I played a pickup game almost every day during college and I really hated to lose, and still do. I always thought of myself as a competitive student as well. I didn't just want to get an A; I wanted to be one of the top students in the class. So yes, I am competitive."

"Good," replied Mike, "Because business owners must enjoy doing whatever it takes to outperform the competition. What it boils down to is that very few products or services are so unique that your customers can't get something comparable elsewhere. You must have a burning need not only to please the customer, but to do it so well your competition finds you unbeatable. This results in higher profits and therefore more money to reinvest in your business so you can continue to win."

"Sounds pretty mercenary," said Tim.

"Well it's not exactly waging war for profit, but it's close. You must enjoy competing and the ability to do whatever it takes to win, which leads to my sixth question: How is your work ethic?"

"Come on, Mike, by now I think you'd see this as an unnecessary question."

"You may think so, but you need to understand that your own business will be a jealous mistress. You're going to be the toughest boss you've ever had, by far. Running your own business is a highly consumptive relationship. It's got to be your passion."

"I'd love to feel that way about my work again," said Tim. "No, I'd say I truly *need* to feel that way about what I do. It's just been so long, I hope I can do it again. I'm starting to understand that being an entrepreneur is really like joining a new religion. Your worldview has a completely new coordinate: your business."

"Well put; you're getting the message loud and clear, so the next question probably is unnecessary."

"Let me have it."

"OK. Are you a good listener? Not just to sages like me," Mike said with a wink. "Now, I know you're good at listening and assimilating information; however, listening to customers, especially when they're unhappy and need to be heard, is an empathetic skill very different from academic learning. Employees are noisy too. Both customers and employees will require you to separate a valid complaint from a whine or a good idea from a bad one. And, most important—and I know this sounds self-serving coming from a lawyer and a CPA—but you'll need to listen intensely to your lawyers and particularly to your accountants. They may seem like luxuries because they're expensive, but you're paying for not only their technical advice but also their wisdom. They've seen it all and know what works. Your own experience as a CPA will be invaluable, but you were a health care specialist, not a business advisory specialist, so you'll still need help."

"I get it, but why are accountants so important?"

"You know," replied Mike, "I always thought I was a good adviser, but honestly I spent too much time plotting my departure. Frankly, I think I've learned more from my accountant than I have through running and selling my businesses."

"That's really surprising, especially with all your experience."

"Not really. Think about it—I finished my accounting and law careers by the time I was thirty-five. A seasoned accountant has helped more businesses and helped engineer more transactions than any entrepreneur ever could. One adviser in particular, my current CPA, Paul Griffin, has given me great, real-world advice, the kind that prevents the big, expensive mistakes, the kind that kill many businesses."

"I have to be a great listener at the hospital," Tim answered. "I couldn't serve my diverse constituents, from doctors to federal regulators, without the ability to actively listen."

"Active listening is a great way to characterize it, because you're constantly making value judgments as you listen, so you can tell if you need to act or if the situation is one that will be best served by a little benign neglect. Of course, the best active listening is practiced by effective salespeople, which leads to my next question: Can you sell?"

"Well, watching how you're slurping up the end of that shake, I think I could sell you a second one," replied Tim. "All kidding aside, I think I can be very persuasive—after all, I got a great girl like Sue to say yes, didn't I?"

Mike smiled and said, "You clearly did a snow job with Sue. In all seriousness, though, very few products or services sell themselves. You need to persuade customers that you deliver the best value. Your product should never be the cheapest, but should always be the most valuable. Selling as a value proposition is a true talent. Selling on price is a race to the bottom—let someone else win."

"I have to admit I don't have much experience selling. I did some at the end of my public accounting career and enjoyed it. It was fun to win."

"There you go—back to the need to win, and sales is clearly all about winning. Although you don't need to be your company's best salesman, you do need to be a key part of the sales effort. Since you haven't found a business yet, this is really a premature question, so I'll state it as more of a requirement."

"Sounds important," said Tim.

"It truly is. To be a successful business owner you must have a skill that adds real value to your business. It really helps if you're the best player at one position or the second-best player at several positions. If you find a technical business, it really helps if you have the required technical skills, and if it's a sales-driven business, you'll need strong sales abilities to effectively lead it. It's hard to lead a business with only strong administrative skills. I've seen many people fail at running a business because their skills added nothing special. It's hard to effectively direct a business when you don't have a deep understanding of what makes it tick. You need the ability to affect outcomes."

"That's interesting, Mike. You know, I've never really thought of business like that. But you're right unless you started the business, you may not have the skills necessary to operate it effectively."

"It's interesting—even people with great skills in a certain area are not necessarily cut out to operate a business centered around those skills."

"By my count that's nine questions; I can't believe you left anything out."

"This last one is easy; we've kind of already talked about it. Do you have a financial goal for your business? You really need to run your business with a long-term goal in mind. It's not enough just to make more money every year, although that's a good start. You need to concentrate on making sure your business is not just a glorified job. You'll want to create real value by developing processes that will make it durable so you can sell it or pass it to your children. We're back to exit velocity."

As they got up to leave, Tim grabbed the check. "Mike, great discussion. This one's definitely on me. I guess the key is to find an appropriate business for sale or start something that's suited to my skills."

"Sums it up. I suggest you discreetly put out some feelers to see if there might be something out there that fits the bill."

The next morning Tim was picking up the Sunday *Enquirer* from the curb when he heard the raspy sound of Mike's Ducati starting up. A few seconds later Mike appeared at the end of his driveway straddling his bright red motorcycle, clad in his worn leathers and a red helmet adorned with a skull and crossbones. This hobby of Mike's, in Tim's estimation, was hard to square with Mike's overly rational worldview, but he had to admit it sure looked like fun. Mike stopped, flipped up his visor, and said, "Tim, I've been thinking a lot about our discussion yesterday and

I think we need to develop a game plan for your search. Like everything else worth doing, this should be done right. I've no lunch plans Tuesday—can you meet?"

"I'll check my calendar; I think so. How about Zino's Firehouse?"

"Works for me—great deep-dish pizza."

"Mike, I can't figure out how an otherwise conservative guy like you can justify motorcycling as a hobby."

"We've discussed this before. I enjoy doing dangerous things carefully. See the knee pucks sewn into these old leathers? Notice anything about them?"

"Nothing remarkable, but then again I've never scrutinized a knee puck before. What should I be looking for?"

"You'll notice the leather is unscratched. I've never taken a corner so fast that I've needed to lean my bike over to the point where my knee is dragging on the pavement. Frankly, I'm just not that good a rider. I know that and ride accordingly. Just like you becoming an entrepreneur. It's dangerous but can be done safely if you take the proper precautions and know your limitations. See you Tuesday at Zino's."

With that, Mike flipped down his visor and sped down the street and around the bend toward Columbia Parkway and the river.

Tim brought the paper into the house, humming a Red Hot Chili Peppers song. Sue heard him and said, "What's gotten into you, humming a tune before you've had your first cup of coffee?"

"You know what? I'm really charged up about the idea of owning my own business. Just imagining a future free from the tyranny of senseless regulations and pointless meetings and having our financial future being determined by a largely disengaged board is incredibly liberating. I may not have been born to be an entrepreneur, but after my discussion with Mike I am convinced I can do it."

"I know Mike told you one of the essential characteristics of being an entrepreneur is to be competitive, and you're that in spades. Owning your own business will put you in a game that you can win. You'll be in control of your own fate, which I know is one of the principal reasons your current job is so physically draining."

"As usual, you're spot on," said Tim. "I'll scramble the eggs if you'll start the coffee."

Chapter Two

THE QUARRY

"You know, Tim, I don't get to Clifton often enough. I suppose I still have negative feelings about the university area because of the three tough years I spent at the University of Cincinnati College of Law. It always seemed like the rest of the students had more money, time, and, as a result, more fun. I felt like I was always running to class, the library, and to my job at the CPA firm."

"Reminds me of one of my dad's favorite sayings, Tim replied. "All work and no play makes Jack."

"Never heard that one before, but it carries more than a grain of truth. Law school gave me a set of skills that allowed me to understand the rules of the game. After I practiced for a few years and developed an even deeper understanding of those rules, I realized that as important as the rules were, one doesn't make the real money until he learns how to play the game successfully. I came to view law and accounting as coaching skills; however, coaches don't make the real money—players do. So I looked for a way into the game as a player, and of course the players were the business owners. I'll admit it became an obsession. Let's order a pizza and talk about how to approach your search."

As they ate, Mike explained how one discreetly trolls for an acquisition. "One of my businesses, the restaurant equipment distributor, is located here in Cincinnati, and we use local CPA and law firms," he said. "I'll talk to Paul Griffin, my CPA, and my lawyer, Jim Williams, and tell them I'm acting as an agent for an undisclosed principal—namely you—who's looking for a business. I think the business should somehow be linked to health care delivery. Do you agree?"

"I guess so; however, I'd like to think my business acumen could add value outside of health care. But I yield to your superior knowledge and experience," Tim said with a smile.

"Tim, I'm a great believer in standing in the shortest line possible. I would think very few buyers of a health-care-related company would add as much value as you."

"When you put it that way, I agree."

"Do you still maintain contact with anyone at your old CPA firm?"

Tim responded, "Yes, I play poker with a group of them once a month."

"Poker? And I had you pegged for a Scrabble player."

"OK, Mr. Ducati, I am allowed to cast myself against type just like you and your knee pucks."

"Touché," Mike replied. "Are any of your fellow players in the business advisory area?"

"Linda Gordon is the partner in charge of that area and one heck of a poker player. When she joined last year the game became coed. We thought the only change would be that the host would need to stock some pinot grigio. However, she really surprised us with her great playing. The stakes have gotten higher and the games tougher. Honestly, she's so strategic she's improved all of our games. Also, we worked together on some very sticky client matters, so I know she can be discreet."

"She sounds perfect. Invite her to lunch and work your search into the conversation. I'm sure someone in her position has helped someone in your position a time or two."

Mike grabbed the check and said, "I've got this one; however, if I find a business you end up buying, you're inviting me to the closing dinner and you're buying . . . and it won't be cheap."

Tim called Linda the next morning and they agreed to meet for coffee that Friday. After debating several spots, they decided to meet at the Caffs & Laffs, an old-school anti-Starbucks owned by Glenda Phillips, a former local TV weather reporter whose slightly offbeat sense of humor played better in her coffeehouse/comedy club than on the local news in conservative Cincinnati.

As they walked in together Linda commented, "You know, I love this place. Glenda is a local treasure and the coffee is great. Someday I'd love to have the requisite tight five minutes and the nerve to go on during open mike night."

"You'd be great. The stand-up CPA. The house would be packed . . . with actuaries."

"Hope that's not your A material, Tim. Get me a latte; I'll find a table.

After sitting down, Tim, jumping right in, said, "I've decided it's time for me to leave corporate America."

"Hope you're not going into comedy and meeting me here was your way to lessen the shock."

"No, I am stone serious—I'd like you to keep your eyes open

for a business for me to buy. Mike Collins, my next-door neighbor and unofficial mentor, thinks it should be health care related, but I don't want to limit the search to only health care. Frankly, I'm open to anything you believe makes sense."

"I agree with Mike. Acquisitions that work, particularly for first-time buyers, like you, generally involve businesses that are closely related to the buyers' current jobs and utilize their existing skills. Of course, experienced buyers—serial entrepreneurs, I call them—become adept at adding value to almost any business. They're just better at the game. Sort of like what the old-time football coach Bum Phillips said about his rival Bear Bryant, the longtime coach of Alabama." Linda, an Alabama graduate, was partial to all things Crimson Tide.

"OK, Linda, what did Bum say?" asked Tim.

"He said Bear was such a good coach he could take his'n and beat your'n or take your'n and beat his'n."

"Not exactly Socrates, but I get it. Would you be willing to put the word out for a so-called undisclosed principal?"

"For you? Anything," replied Linda. "I'd like to see you get wealthy so I could relieve you of even more of your money at the poker table. By the way, how's Sue feel about this?"

"She's thrilled. Evidently, I've been a bit hard to deal with as I've fallen out of love with my job, and she's right. You know, the more I think of leaving, the more I realize I've viewed my job as a sentence, with retirement being my release date."

"Happens. I've noticed your steps have lost some spring. I think she's right—you need a change. I think I know you well enough to say that while you may be a reluctant entrepreneur, you'll be a good one."

"Thanks, I think."

"I don't want to get too personal, but have you given any thought as to size?"

"Not really, Tim replied. "I guess I'd like it to be big enough to support my family in the manner to which they've become accustomed, but small enough that I could pull the deal off alone."

"Not a lot of guidance, but you know me—I can color outside the lines."

"Thanks, Linda. Call me when you've got either a lead on a business or that tight five minutes and I'll catch you at open mike night."

"OK, and thanks for the latte. I'll stay in touch, and don't worry, I'll be discreet."

Tim trusted that Linda would, as promised, put out some discreet feelers. Unlike most people, she actually went out of her way to help people, even when there was absolutely nothing in it for her. That is probably why she is so good at her job. Her service ethic borders on a religious calling, and people love her for it.

It was Friday night, the start of the long Independence Day weekend, when Tim pulled his car into his driveway. Since all three of his family's cars were randomly and strategically parked like a slalom course to block his access to the garage, he gave up and parked his car on the street. Since he was this close to Mike's house, he decided to stop in to see if Mike was going to be around for the holiday weekend. Tim was about to ring the doorbell when he noticed Mike popping out of his pool, having concluded his nightly one-mile swim. By the time Tim got to the fence surrounding the pool Mike had pulled his goggles to the top of his head and was walking toward him. Tim could hear Jimi Hendrix coming through the earbuds attached to Mike's goggles. "Water ballet to the tune of 'Purple Haze'?" Tim inquired.

"Glad to see your sense of humor is back . . . I think. I'm about to indulge in a post-swim refreshment—want to join me?"

"Sure, maybe I'll get lucky and someone will see my car on the street and reorganize the driveway maze."

"So, did you find a business yet?"

"I'm not sure," replied Tim. On Tuesday I'm meeting with my friend Linda. She said she has something to show me. Since we started this process six weeks ago I've kissed my share of frogs, so I am a bit skeptical."

"Yeah, sorry I've not been more help. The process can be pretty lengthy, particularly if you're not able to hunt full-time. What kind of businesses have you been looking at?"

"A bit of everything, from a chain of yogurt shops to a metal plating business. Nothing seems to feel right."

"I think you'll know when it's the right one," said Mike. "It's like what Supreme Court Justice Potter Stewart said about pornography: 'I can't describe it but I know it when I see it.'"

"Mike, in all our discussions you've been sort of vague about the size of business I should be looking for. I can't believe you don't have a strong opinion about that."

"Oddly enough, I really don't. If it fits and it's small, you should be able to grow it. If it fits and it's big, you'll just need to be creative about financing. I didn't want you concentrating on something that may be irrelevant."

"I should have known; you're always looking out for me."

"I just want to focus on the right things is all. Go grill some dogs for that hungry family of yours. Marcia and I are headed to our son Jim's house for a cookout, which means I'll be watching the grill like a hawk so I don't have to eat a piece of tanned hide. Jim's attention to the grilling details is unfortunately secondary to choosing the appropriate wine. I told him nothing goes with leather except shoe polish."

That Tuesday Tim arrived at the Caffs & Laffs a little early and used the time to think about what life might be like being the master of his own destiny. It made him smile; he was definitely looking forward to being engaged and building his own much bigger future.

"What's with the sly smile?" asked Linda. "Did you find a meter with time left on it?"

"Nice to see you too, Linda. No, I just have a good feeling about our meeting today. You've got my future in your portfolio, I just feel it."

"Maybe, but since this business is represented by a broker who's prepared a book, you'll have to sign a nondisclosure agreement before I can show it to you."

Tim read through the three-page document that prevented him from disclosing the information contained in the book. Not being entirely familiar with such an agreement, he asked, "Is this all standard? It doesn't look any more obnoxious than most legal documents I've seen."

"Yeah, it follows most of them. You can show the book to your advisers, but no one else."

As he signed the document he said to Linda, "Right, no problem. Let's see the book."

"Well, it's a little pricey, but it's right up your alley." As Tim flipped through the book, Linda continued, "The company, Revenue Cycle Associates—they call themselves RCA—provides consulting services to hospitals to improve their revenue cycle through staff augmentation. They also—"

Tim stopped her. "I know this company well. We've used them often at the hospital. They do excellent work. Why is it for sale?"

"My client Pete Grove, the owner, tells me he is ready for his next challenge. He's sixty-two, healthy, and wants a few years off before moving on to his next deal. It seems like true entrepreneurs like Pete don't know how to hit anything but the pause button. He bought RCA five years ago, doubled the sales, and tripled the bottom line. He thinks it's a good point to exit. The price would represent a nice return for him. He deserves it based upon how he's enhanced the company's performance."

"Linda, I know I can't expect you to reveal anything about his price expectations since it would be a conflict of interest, but did he run any of this by you before the broker put the price in the book?"

"Of course; however, I really can't be any more evaluative than that. You understand."

After they finished their coffee Tim got up to leave and added, "Should I direct questions to you or the broker?"

"I am out of it at this point. All future communication should be between you and your advisers and the broker. If we move to a letter of intent, usually the lawyers do most of the back-and-forth. Good luck with this, Tim. It will be fun to sort of work together on something." Linda punctuated the last statement with a wink that had Tim's mental gears turning on his way back to his car.

Tim sneaked a couple of peeks at the book while at work, dying to dig into it once he got home.

"Sue, I've got our future in my hands," Tim proclaimed as he walked through the door. "What I've got right here is the future Turner family business. I suggest you summon your considerable creative powers and design an appropriate crest for the wrought iron gate that will be guarding the entrance to our vast estate."

Although Sue was happy to see Tim back to his old self, she had been secretly worried about his quest being in vain. She knew other friends who had tried to buy or start businesses with disastrous results. However, she knew if times really got tough she could easily revive her career as a graphic designer. She'd done a significant amount of freelance work since the twins were in high school, and she had no problem landing good assignments.

"I am going to take this book into my office. I've only had a chance to glance at it between meetings like a kid who sneaked a comic book into class. It would have been a hard thing to explain away if I got caught. Kind of exciting, really." With that Tim closed the door to his small study off the living room. It was the one room in the house in which Sue had given him free rein. It had all Tim's favorite books, a killer stereo, Reds memorabilia, a couple of Remington bronzes, a wet bar, and of course a flat screen TV. Everything a man could want and then some, as far as Tim was concerned.

Sue called Tim for dinner and as he walked in she noticed he looked pensive. "So, good news or bad news?"

"Good question," he replied.

Sue could tell by Tim's demeanor some of the air had been let out of the new business balloon.

"First the good news. The business, Revenue Cycle Associates, is right up my alley. I know what they do since we use them at the hospital. They've got a well-deserved reputation for delivering excellent service, they're growing nicely and profitably, and I've even got an idea that would really help their business grow."

"Wow, that's almost too good to be true. What's the bad news?"

"Take a guess," Tim said.

"Price."

"You got it in one. I can't possibly afford a $3 million price tag. Sue, as we discussed last year when we were doing our estate planning, our net worth is around $1.5 million with about $500,000 that's in marketable securities that are not part of our retirement accounts, and that's mostly in the bank stock my dad gifted us, which has a really low basis."

"What's the significance of that?" asked Sue.

"It just means if we were to sell it to invest in the business we would owe big-time capital gains tax. You know, Mike told me I should only be concerned about finding a business that fit, one where I could add significant value, and not to worry about the size. So I find one, and can't see how I can possibly afford it. It's a real disappointment."

"Tim, I know you're disappointed that you can't just write a check, but you've always lived by the maxim that you can't be afraid to pay for value. It seems like this company may fall into the real value category. Maybe Mike will have some ideas."

"You're right. I guess I kind of knew when I finally got to the page with the price it was going to be high, since the company's performance was so good; just not quite that high. I know Mike is out of town until Friday. I'll e-mail him some of the essential information and see if he'll agree to stop by Friday evening for a strategy session.

"It's times like this I really miss my dad," Tim continued. "I could really use his insight right now. Even though he never really put his own money at risk, I always admired how he analyzed deals in which the bank participated. Those couple of summers I worked for him during college he'd occasionally let me sit in on a customer meeting. I remember that he could always cut to the nub of the deal quicker than the accountants or lawyers at the meeting. I always had the feeling the buyer, who was usually the bank's customer, was glad Dad was in their corner and not the seller's."

"That business insight rubbed off," said Sue. "Not only from those meetings but also from your dinner discussions. I remember a few of those got pretty deep into the business weeds. I think you inherited great business judgment from your dad."

"Thanks. I guess we'll know that's true if I'm able to put this deal together."

Before turning in that night Tim sent Mike a long e-mail detailing RCA's essential business and financial information along with the asking price, and inviting him over for a cigar and a glass of wine on Friday night.

The next morning Tim checked his e-mail before he left for work and saw Mike had already responded with "CALL ME FIRST THING IN THE MORNING!" Tim noticed that the e-mail had been sent only minutes before, so instead of calling Mike, he walked over and rang the Collinses' doorbell. Mike answered, dressed in his bicycling attire. "Looks like you got an active morning ahead," Tim said enviously.

"Yeah, I'm meeting some of my fellow ancient road warriors at the Little Miami bike trail. Before you get too impressed, we only bike twenty miles or so and then we hit Busken Bakery and eat our weight in doughnuts. I'm sure we don't even get close to breaking even." He continued, "Well, Tim, my analysis of RCA's information leads me to believe you've found a great opportunity. Certainly meets the most important criteria."

"I know. I should be able to add value, right?"

"You live revenue cycle management every day," said Mike.

"It gets better. I know from dealing with some of RCA's competitors that there's a new product line I'd like to add, which will make the company more competitive and should increase sales and profits dramatically."

"Instead of our usual Friday evening cigar, why don't you and your family come over for dinner Friday night and I'll give you my thoughts? Between now and then you need to do some soul-searching on your risk tolerance. I recall from our lunch at Aglamesis that you believe you can eat risk for a midmorning snack. Well, this deal will force you to prove that."

"I look forward to Friday, Mike." As Tim walked to his car he said over his shoulder, "Have a good ride and enjoy those killer cinnamon doughnuts."

On his way to work Tim thought about Mike's warning. This kind of risk did make him a bit queasy, but it was a good kind of queasy, like he'd felt before his first date with Sue.

Tim called Sue from his car to confirm Friday. He was mentally compiling his list of questions for Mike as he walked into the hospital. Once he reached his office it hit him that compared to running his own business, his current job was little more than acting as a glorified referee for the hospital's needlessly complex administrative function. His job was not fulfilling and had no real upside. It was feeling more and more like he was serving hard time, particularly when compared to the liberating idea of owning his own business. He hoped he wasn't kidding himself not only about RCA, but about the whole idea of owning his own business. He was now having a very difficult time imagining himself as anything but an entrepreneur.

Chapter Three

PREGAME

It was a rare cool, dry July evening in Cincinnati, perfect for a cookout. Although Tim was looking forward to picking Mike's brain about the RCA deal, he had to admit he was also excited about the prospect of a gourmet dinner on the Collinses' deck. Their great view of the city, east to Lunken Airport and west to downtown and Great American Ball Park, seemed to inspire Tim to think big. Mike's optimism didn't hurt either. The Turner family arrived promptly at six thirty, none with one arm as long as the other, thanks to Tim's mom's long-ago warning of the rudeness of arriving at a dinner party empty-handed. Tim had selected a pinot noir blush to complement the salmon Mike was grilling. Bringing wine to the Collinses' was always a challenge, since Mike was a connoisseur with very specific criteria for food and wine pairings.

"Look at this good-looking group," Mike commented as the Turners filed into the Collinses' awe-inspiring entry hall. Tim always marveled at how walking into their house felt like you were making a final approach in a small aircraft over the hills of northern Kentucky. "Marcia, it looks like a group right out of the Sears catalog, doesn't it?" Mike said with the goofy grin he seemed to save for his closest friends.

Marcia, casting a disdainful eye at Mike, responded, "Sears catalog . . . really, Mike, talk about dating yourself. I bet the twins have never even seen one, have you?"

Seth and Kim looked at each other quizzically and both shook their heads. Still on the verbal assault, Marcia quipped, "See? Better update your cultural allusions so folks under fifty have some idea what you're talking about, Mike—or should I say Grandpa Walton?"

"Enough of this—let's celebrate Tim's rare find, a business that fits," Mike stated with his wineglass raised.

Marcia and Sue went into the kitchen to put the finishing touches on the side dishes as Tim and Mike performed their manly grilling function at Mike's spectacular grill, built into a stone wall next to an outdoor fireplace. "I have to admit, Mike, every time we grill out here I feel like you should be putting a giant rack of ribs on that stone grill like Fred Flintstone."

"I don't think that would get past the cholesterol police. Although one of these nights we'll do it," Mike said wistfully. "Tim, I've had a chance to review your e-mail thoroughly and I meant what I said when you came in; I really believe RCA is a great opportunity for you," he continued as he expertly checked the temperature of the salmon.

"I hope you're right. You've seen my financial statement. I can't afford to make a major mistake," Tim said as he looked through the glass doors into Mike's study, where the twins were shooting pool.

"You're right. You've still got, what, at least one more year of college tuition for those two? Plus, most likely grad school. We'll work it out so your risk will be minimal. I've got an idea already. No more business talk until after dinner." Mike knocked on the kitchen window and yelled to Marcia, "Fish is ready, time to eat!"

The conversation was free-flowing as the families enjoyed the food and beautiful evening. Seth pushed away from the table and proclaimed, "You know, Mr. Collins, your house reminds me of a five-star resort. Someday I'm going to own a place like this."

Kim gave him the withering stare sisters reserve for their brothers and said, "Fat chance."

"Save your money, study hard, work hard, and I'll sell you this one," Mike said somewhat seriously.

As Tim was taking in this exchange he let himself imagine being in the financial position to own a home like the Collinses'. He knew it was a lofty goal, and like so many other goals, one he'd never achieve without taking the plunge and buying his own business. The more he let this fantasy invade his thoughts, the less like fantasy it seemed. It was more like *when* and less like *if*.

After dinner Mike invited Tim into his expansive study. It looked like a step back into the 1920s. In addition to the beautiful pool table, Mike had an extensive collection of antique Stickley furniture beautifully arranged on a couple of stunning rugs from the arts and crafts era and, completing the effect, oversize palms strategically placed throughout the room. "Mike, I just love this room. I feel like we walked onto the set of *The Sting*. This is the kind of straightforward decorating I can understand." Tim noticed Mike was smiling broadly as he opened his humidor and selected two Diamond Crown Churchills for them.

As he was cutting the cigars Mike said, "Yeah, I love this room, but I always thought something was missing for this place next to my humidor, and then last week I noticed an antique armillary sphere in the window of an antique store in Covington. It's being delivered tomorrow. I can't wait."

"Funny how we go from comic books and pocket knives to antiques and motorcycles, isn't it?"

"You've got to be careful or you can get pretty caught up in it. It's much better to collect assets that yield a return and appreciate, like good companies." Mike handed Tim his cigar as he flipped his table lighter. As Tim was puffing Mike continued, "I don't want to get too deep into this tonight, but there are a couple of really important aspects that you need to bear in mind as you move forward."

"I'm all ears."

"The first thing is the asking price of $3 million—way too high. Not even close to this company's value."

"Why would they price it too high?" asked Tim.

"Pricing small companies is a game to some brokers. They seem to operate under the greater fool theory. Unlike the stock market, which operates in a fairly efficient fashion in that anyone with a computer can know instantly what any listed company is worth, the value of a privately held company, particularly one as small as RCA, is hard to peg because it's so difficult to find comparables."

"Not like home buying, is it?"

"Not at all," Mike answered. Buyers and their brokers can put any number they want on a business and since you can't look up a comparable on MLS, unsophisticated buyers can be duped into paying too high a price. Smallish brokers, like the one representing RCA, that sell a lot of what I call owner-operator businesses make a fundamental mistake."

"What's that?

"Instead of showing EBITDA—short for earnings before interest, taxes, depreciation, and amortization—which is the standard valuation metric, they show SDCF, or seller's discretionary cash flow. EBITDA is the best starting point for determining value, since it determines the company's ability to pay off the purchase price and provide a return to the new owner. SDCF, on the other hand, is really a pretty subjective measure. And as a result, the asking price is more often predicated on what the seller thinks he needs rather than what the business is really worth. Kind of reminds me of those old cartoon car races where the character driving the slower car draws in higher numbers on his speedometer so he can win."

"Yeah, I've never heard of SDCF," said Tim. "My experience with transactions is pretty limited. However, the hospital has purchased some medical practices, and those deals are usually more about what percentage of future production the docs keep. The acquisition price is really secondary."

"Yes, buying an operating business is really nothing like that; however, the flaw in looking at SDCF is that the number reflects cash flow before the owners are paid anything. For very small businesses there is generally very little cash flow after the owner has been paid a market rate salary, so brokers like to use this concept since it makes the company look more profitable to an unsophisticated buyer. This metric is really only appropriate for buyers trying to buy a job like a paper route. However, in a larger business like this, where a buyer is not just looking to buy a job, the appropriate bottom-line metric is adjusted EBIDTA."

"OK, makes sense, I guess. But why an adjusted EBIDTA?"

"Two things, really. First, it shows the actual post-closing cash flow available for paying the acquisition debt and for the new owner's compensation, as well as providing a return on capital invested. All the expenses related to the current owner are removed. I guess I've used this concept so much in transactions I forget it's really not self-explanatory."

"So are you just adjusting out unnecessary expenses?"

"Sort of. The goal is to determine the amount of cash flow after you take over. That's why it's the correct indicator of value."

"So you take out all the expenses that are not required to operate the business, like the current owner's perks?"

"That's right," replied Mike. "But you also need to subtract what your cost to operate the business will be, including the cost of replacing the current owner. Remember, SDCF ascribes no value to the owner's contribution."

"I see—even though it's supposedly discretionary doesn't mean the seller didn't have a significant role in producing the company's results," Tim added, warming to the idea.

"Now you've got it. Often owners do the job of two or three people, people you'll need to hire. So, SDCF is almost never a good proxy for profitability."

"OK, so what's the second item?"

"Pricing for companies is commonly based on multiples of EBITDA. Even smaller companies like RCA."

"OK, but why is that pertinent here?" asked Tim.

"Even though RCA's a small company, there is a very active market in healthcare-related consulting companies, and as a result, there will be some data available for market value multiples based on recent transactions. So, for example, let's say you find the proper multiple is four and the adjusted EBITDA is $500,000. The value would be $2 million."

"So there will be information regarding the multiples of EBIDTA that companies like RCA sold for?"

"Yes, your accounting firm will have access to various databases they use when they do business valuations."

"Maybe I should engage them to do a business valuation of RCA."

"Not necessary. Once your CPA has analyzed RCA's financial information, he'll be able to give you a good indication of value without doing a formal valuation."

"Thanks, Mike. As usual, your real world insights are not only on point but fill in my sizable knowledge gap. I really appreciate the interest you've taken in my project."

"My pleasure. One last thing before we conclude tonight's business. I think it's time to formally engage your CPA. I strongly suggest Paul Griffin, and once you think you're ready to make an offer, you'll need a lawyer, which of course means you'll be spending some real money. Although I'm a big believer in OPM—that is, other people's money, like a bank or the current owner—when buying a business, you will still need to determine how much cash you're willing to risk in this deal. Of course, the bank is also going to require an unlimited personal guarantee."

"I'm expecting that, but I have to admit it is a scary thought."

"It should be, but like I said at Aglamesis, you need to understand your relationship with your money. The money you're going to spend with your professionals will add real value, even if you don't do the deal."

"Why is that?" asked Tim.

"Old saying: Sometimes the best deals are the ones you don't make. The understanding of the process you'll gain is worth at least part of the price of admission. Although I wouldn't put a high probability on it, you need to understand you could go through almost the entire process and end up with nothing but more experience and less money. I've seen a few buyers get irate over these expenses and want the seller to refund them. That, of course, is never part of an offer letter, which, as you know from your hospital deals, is called a letter of intent, or an LOI for short."

"Not like swapping out a few baseball cards, is it?"

"No," replied Mike. "You could easily spend $10,000-$15,000 dollars and end up with no deal."

"Sobering thought, but I'm ready."

"Good. I hope you still feel that way after I explain one more very important concept." Mike pointed his cigar at Tim for emphasis.

"Sounds serious."

"It is. You need to give real thought not only to the cash you're going to risk but also to the debt you're going to guarantee."

"Mike, I've been handling the hospital's $25 million bank facility for years. I know the drill," Tim said somewhat defensively.

He did, however, resist the temptation to point his cigar at Mike.

"I understand that, but I've seen entrepreneurs take on significant debt to fund some pretty suspect growth plans, or worse, to fund the losses of a doomed business in a weak economy."

"Bad ideas, both."

"You bet," Mike agreed. "It seems like business owners, whether because of hubris or desperation, forget you have to pay back every dollar borrowed with after-tax cash. It was particularly bad back when banks were lending massive amounts of airball money."

"Air ball?"

"Cute phrase. Means debt unsupported by hard assets or receivables—air. . . . Get it?"

"Helpful with an acquisition," said Tim, "but I could see where that would be a dangerous choice for capital when a company is experiencing tough times."

"Exactly. Your next step is to talk to the broker and see if you'll be allowed access to all their financial information before you sign an LOI."

"You mean I may need to come up with a price before I see any more information?" Tim said incredulously.

"You might—actually, I'd say it's likely. Brokers and sellers don't like tire kickers."

"How can I do that, since, as you put it, SDCF figures aren't helpful in determining value?"

"There are two things you can do. One, put a broad range in the LOI for the price, or use
   the technique I prefer."

"What's that?" Tim said with some hope of clearing up this disturbing point.

"The LOI will present a price as a multiple of a figure that you and your advisers determine through a thorough inspection of the seller's information known as due diligence, to be the correct figure for adjusted EBITDA. Remember, Paul's firm will give you a multiple or at least a tight range of multiples of EBITDA that represent a fair estimation of value."

"So, part of my CPA's due diligence work will be arriving at the proper adjusted EBITDA figure?"

"Exactly."

"I get it," Tim said as he walked toward their wives, who were enjoying the cool night air.

When the wives saw the men approaching, they cut off their conversation and Sue asked, "Did you gentlemen have a good discussion?"

Just as the two men were about to sit down at the chairs surrounding the outdoor fireplace, fireworks boomed over Great American Ball Park. "Another Reds home run," Mike said with some pride.

"You've really adopted the Reds since you've moved here from Nashville, Mike."

"It's hard not to like a young team that tries hard every night and never gives up. Also good traits for a new entrepreneur," Mike said with a wink.

"Sue, as usual, Mike set my mind right, just like Cool Hand Luke. It's been quite a lesson. Clearly my experience with acquisitions hasn't prepared me for buying my own business. Now I understand what needs to be done. I just hope I'm up to the task."

"You'll do fine, and good advisers like Paul will make it seem easy. He guided me through some pretty dicey deals. You just need to remember two important items: It's only money, but it's your money; and nothing in business defies logic, even pricing and buying companies."

"You're right, I know I can't afford to get emotionally wrapped up in making a deal I can't afford."

While walking home Tim was whistling as Kim put her arm around her dad and said, "I think you're very lucky to have struck up a friendship with Mike. You always seem happy after you've met with him."

"You're right, Kim. Something about Mike's demeanor and attitude really instills confidence."

"I can tell, Pop. I'm sure you'll be a great entrepreneur. What have you ever not been great at . . . except maybe golf?"

"Thanks—I think," Tim said as he hugged his daughter and chuckled.

Chapter Four

GETTING COACHED

The next morning before he started on the lawn, Tim decided to call Linda at home.

"Hello," Linda answered, somewhat out of breath.

"Sorry, Linda, it's Tim—did I catch you mid-workout?"

"Yeah, I am actually still on my elliptical, but I can talk if you don't mind a little panting."

"I could say something inappropriate here, but since I'm going to ask you for a favor, I'd better not."

"Exercising good judgment for a change—you must have a tall order."

"Kind of," Tim said plaintively, without explaining any further.

"Don't get quiet on me now—you've called me at home on a business matter and disrupted my workout," Linda said sarcastically.

"I had a long talk with Mike last night and he thinks there's some critical information I need to have reviewed before I present a letter of intent."

"I like the sound of the LOI—what do you need?"

"According to Mike—and after hearing his logic, I agree—I'm going to need enough financial information to determine what my cash flow would be after a purchase. Mike called it adjusted EBITDA. The SDCF in the book doesn't provide enough information since the market data available is all based on EBITDA multiples."

"I understand. I didn't agree with how that was presented either. Normally the seller wouldn't allow any type of due diligence until there was a signed LOI, but since I know you're a serious buyer I think I can convince Pete that it's OK."

"Thanks, Linda, you can plug your earbuds back in and crank up the Manilow."

"It's actually Michael Bublé, so you weren't even close. Talk to you Monday."

On Monday Linda called Tim back and gave him the green light. "Pete said he'll make the information to determine your post-acquisition cash flow available. Are you going to handle this yourself?"

"No, anticipating your persuasiveness, I am having lunch today with Paul Griffin. Paul and his firm do a lot of work with business buyers and sellers. Mike Collins strongly recommended him."

"Yeah, I've heard he does a lot of mergers and acquisitions."

"Mike's used him on a couple of matters and says he's really good, but not cheap."

"You know my motto, Tim—good and cheap doesn't exist in the world of professionals, only at outlet malls and then only if you exercise extreme patience."

"Once I talk to Paul, could you set up a time for him to meet with Pete and get the information?"

"Pete will probably want Paul to come to my office. I've got all the information here, so it'll be much less disruptive."

"Makes sense. I'll call you after lunch."

"OK, Tim. This is getting pretty exciting, isn't it?"

"It is, but I've got the feeling it's also about to get expensive as well."

"Paying for top-flight professionals out of your own pocket is something you're going to need to get used to."

"Don't get me wrong. I know I need expert assistance, and I know from Mike's unqualified endorsement Paul can provide it. Mike's already worked me over on that point. At this critical juncture I'm happy to pay to get the information and advice I know I need."

"Wow, you are truly the big boy."

"Thanks for your help on this. I'll call after lunch."

Tim sat at a table near the window at the Echo, a small throwback diner right off Hyde Park Square. As he was looking at the menu he saw Paul walk in. In his custom-made suit and shirt, Paul looked more like Wall Street than Hyde Park Square. The look fit his reputation to a tee. "Paul, I am surprised you didn't want to meet at one of the trendier restaurants on the square," Tim said as Paul sat down.

"Well, Tim, you're not a paying client yet, so I'm watching costs," Paul said with a smirk.

"Smart move, the implication being that you're buying."

"Of course. Also I'm a big fan of the potpie here. Everything's good—just avoid the Jell-O; it's only on the menu for the older clientele." Paul motioned toward several tables in the back of the restaurant filled with obvious retirees who, sure enough, were finishing off their early bird lunches with lime Jell-O."

"So, Paul, I've found a company I'd like to take a run at. I've gotten the book from Linda Gordon, a CPA at my former firm, who has worked with the company for the past five years."

"Since you said there's a book, I assume there's a broker involved."

"Yes, Linda is pretty much staying out of it, except she's agreed to ask Pete Grove, the owner, if we could do some limited due diligence before we submit an LOI."

"I suppose that's where I come in?"

"Correct. I'd like your help turning the SDCF numbers presented in the book into adjusted EBITDA so I'd have a better basis for establishing a fair price. And, if possible, I'd like your opinion on the proper value of the company."

"Happy to help. As you probably know, my firm does a lot of transaction work from both the buyer's and seller's sides, so we know what we're looking for and we'll be very efficient."

"I appreciate that," said Tim. "It probably goes without saying, but I am trying to limit my investment until I know I can put this deal together."

"Understood. Getting a handle on the real EBITDA is critical; we get that. We also understand that particularly as a first-time buyer, you'll need some help with the negotiations, tax structure, and financing. I also know you're friends with Mike Collins, who's helping you out. We'll happily fill in where you need us."

"Thanks, Paul. Don't blush, but you're every bit as professional as I've heard you were." As the steaming potpie was served, Tim added, "I hope you were also right about the potpie."

"If you don't like it I'll finish it off for you in addition to paying for it."

Tim continued, "I've been given the names of a couple of lawyers I could use in this transaction. Do you have someone you'd recommend?"

"I've worked a lot with Jim Williams. Smart, fast, done a ton of deals, but not cheap."

"Sounds like your bio," said Tim.

"Thanks, I think."

As Paul grabbed the check and paid at the register, Tim walked outside. Paul caught up with him and they walked toward the square, where both their cars were parked. "Any room for a Graeter's ice cream cone?" asked Tim. "I'm buying."

"No time; I'll save the calories for the closing dinner. Call me after you hear from Linda." Paul hit his Mercedes key fob and popped open the door. Before getting in he added, "I've got some time available this week and next; after that I'm wall-to-wall for several weeks."

"Gotcha. Hope I get good news this afternoon."

Later that afternoon Linda called Tim's cell. Tim, recognizing the number, answered the phone and with a total lack of etiquette said, "What's the word, Linda?"

"Hello to you too, Tim."

"Sorry, I didn't mean to be so boorish. Just getting excited, I guess."

"Well, I've got good news. Pete's going to allow you and your advisers to see the last five years' financial statements, tax returns, and any other financial information you may need."

"That's great, but I would think Paul may still have some questions in order to arrive at a good adjusted EBITDA figure."

"He probably will, but Pete's given me the OK to provide whatever you want. If I don't have the answer, he said he'd make himself available whenever you need him."

"Very accommodating," said Tim. "I don't expect you to breach confidentiality, but can you disclose how many of the offering books went out?"

"The brokers are handling that, and I know from working with them before that they consider the number of books requested to be a good indication of the demand for the company. I also know they believe the more interested buyers, the higher the price, and, perhaps counterintuitively, the less time to close. According to them, urgency equals currency. Anyway, ten books are out."

"Any information on the recipients?"

"Not anything specific. A couple went to the usual suspects," Linda replied.

"Meaning?"

"Early retirees from national companies. I don't think RCA's really up their alley. Also a couple of private equity firms that have health care companies in their portfolios."

"Mike thinks RCA would be a little small for a PE firm."

"Probably, but maybe not, if they already have a company in their portfolio that RCA fits with so well they could do a tuck-in."

"A tuck-in?"

"Sorry—that is insider lingo for a smaller company that is in the same business as one of the companies the private equity firm already owns."

"I guess all I can do is figure out RCA's worth to me and not hallucinate about what other buyers might pay."

"You're right, Tim. However, this is such a good fit for you that you may want to stretch a bit."

"Selling now, are you, Linda?"

"A little, but I'd really like to see you buy RCA. Feels right to me."

Tim called Paul next, who promised to call Linda and see if they couldn't get going immediately.

Paul called back a few minutes later. "Tim, it's all set up. I'll e-mail an engagement letter to you. It'll be pretty broad in its scope, like, 'All activities associated with the due diligence for the potential acquisition of RCA'. I estimate the cost to be five thousand for this pricing phase. If I think it will be more after I see the information, I'll let you know."

"What will your report look like?" asked Tim.

"We'll show a yearly reconciliation between the SDCF and what, in our opinion, represents an accurate adjusted EBITDA figure. This will allow you to make an offer based on market data that we access. I'll include plenty of explanation."

"Perfect. I look forward to hearing from you. I'll print out the engagement letter, sign it, and scan it. Do you want me to mail a hard copy?"

"Please do," replied Paul. "We've done this sort of analysis many times, so we'll get the report to you quickly."

"Thanks, Paul. By the way, I know you'd think as a financial professional and a CPA I'd be fairly well versed in deals, but I'm not, so please draft it as a 'Deals for Dummies' guide."

"Will do, Tim."

After hanging up, Tim felt a nervous twitch in his stomach. He'd never paid a professional for anything except a simple estate plan a few years back that had cost $1000. Now with one phone call he'd authorized a $5,000 engagement. He now knew how his clients had felt. He had to admit he'd lacked a little empathy when he worked for a CPA firm. Just one of the many revelations resulting from this process, he supposed.

A few days later Paul called. "Tim, we've completed the report. I'll send it to your personal e-mail address. Take a look at it. I think it's pretty self-explanatory; however, I suggest we get together once you and Mike have analyzed it. I included our certified valuation analyst's, Doug Edwards's, opinion of value. I am sure you and Mike will have your own opinions."

Tim decided to wait until he got home to open the e-mail, partly because he knew he would not be able to get anything done if he opened it now and partly because, he had to admit, he was nervous about what he would see. Analyzing his own emotions, he couldn't tell if he was more worried that it would look good and he would be moving forward or if he would be disappointed because it looked bad and he would need to start over.

That night over dinner he explained the process to Sue, who, as usual, took the pragmatic approach. "I know you've got your hopes up, but this isn't like choosing a golf partner; there's no politics involved. It's a straight-up business call—either you can make a deal at the right price or you can't. Analyze it, sleep on it, and spend some time with Mike. Is he in town?"

"Yes. I'll forward the report to him tonight with my comments. I sure hope he has some time tomorrow night to go over it."

"Marcia told me she thinks Mike's as excited about this as you are. I'm sure he'll make time to get together."

Tim retired to his study, powered up his computer, opened Paul's e-mail, and printed out the report (Appendix A).

Tim read the report twice and understood why the 6.5 multiple was used. He also understood the need to add excess working capital to the price. However, he did not know how RCA's at-closing balance sheet would affect the offer price. Tim was aware that structuring the deal as an asset purchase would allow him to buy only certain assets and assume only certain liabilities, whereas if the deal was structured as a stock purchase, he would be buying the balance sheet intact.

Sue walked into Tim's study as he was mulling over Paul's number. "So how's it look?"

"Well, based on this analysis, I'd guess the offering price should be considerably less than the $3 million."

"How much less?"

"Paul's report indicates the asset value to be approximately $1.8 million. But I don't know how the balance sheet figures in. That is, I don't know which assets I'll be buying or which liabilities I'll be required to assume."

"I guess I understand most of that, which is good, but what's more important is I know you understand all of it," Sue said with a chuckle. "Will Mike be able to help you sort this out?"

"I'm counting on it. I plan on calling him tomorrow for his thoughts."

"All sounds encouraging. Let's have a beer on the porch and dream of vast wealth."

"Financial freedom would be enough for me. I'll be right out—I am going to add my notes to the report before I forward it to Mike."

"OK," replied Sue. "Meet you outside."

Tim made his notes on the report and forwarded it to Mike.

_____

Chapter Five

GAME TIME

Before heading to work the next morning, Tim checked his e-mail for Mike's response. As usual, it was terse:

Tim, about what I expected. Balance sheet is pretty strong, but I think that's in your favor. I'll call you later. —Mike

Just before noon Mike called. "Tim, I like what I saw. Obviously the deductions needed to arrive at adjusted EBITDA were significant, as expected."

"Yeah, Mike, you were right—SDCF included no deduction for compensation paid to the owner."

"I thought Paul's partner Doug's valuation information was very helpful. He did a thorough job. Stop by tonight and we'll hash this out."

With the twins back at college, Tim and Sue got into the habit of eating dinner at their kitchen island, but they resisted the urge to watch TV as they ate, even though the relative quiet of being empty nesters was unnerving at times. Between bites Sue said, "Seth called today wondering if there was going to be a high-paying job for him at RCA soon."

"I guess that's a possibility and really fun to think about, but it seems like it's a long way down the pike."

"Maybe to you, but you know how much he respects you. I think you'd be great working together."

"First I've got to put this deal together. I'm going over to Mike's tonight to come up with a price."

"Once you've arrived at a price, what's next?"

"I'll put together a letter of intent to submit my offer."

"Will you use Mike's lawyer, Jim Williams, for that?"

"I've done a lot of checking around and he has great credentials. I've been on the other side of the table from him when the hospital has acquired a few physician practices and found him to be smart, fair, and he doesn't miss anything."

"Have you contacted him yet?"

"No, I'll call Jim tomorrow if we can agree on a number tonight."

As Tim was walking out the door Sue called after him, "I'll be happy to kick in my First Communion money if that helps."

"As tight as you are, I know you have that stashed away somewhere. Hope we don't need it, but thanks for the offer."

Mike greeted Tim at the door with his readers on, papers in hand and ready for action. "Welcome to the war room, Tim. Let's buy a company." Mike led Tim into his study, where he had Tim's deal spread over his massive desk.

"I'm ready."

"Getting right to it," Mike said. "So here's how we should put together your offer. We'll use $300,000 for the EBITDA, 6.5 for the multiple, and add to it the $500,000 of excess working capital to get to a total value of $2,450,000.

"Why $300,000 and not the $288, 000 shown on the report?"

"I liked the idea of a deduction for the board of advisers' fee; I just think $40,000 is a little steep for a company RCA's size."

"Yeah, I thought that was a little high myself."

"OK, now time to factor in how the balance sheet will affect how you'll pay the purchase price. You'll notice Paul's at-closing balance sheet excludes the cash."

"Yeah, Paul's report indicated the seller usually keeps the cash."

"That's true, and even though deals are usually done cash-free and debt-free, I'd suggest you assume RCA's accounts payable and accrued expenses. So we'll let Pete keep his cash, but we won't assume the $50,000 in long-term debt. Pete will need to pay that off himself from the sales proceeds. OK, so your offer will be for $2,450,000, $685,000 of which will be paid by assuming liabilities; the balance will be paid partly in cash and partly in a note to the seller."

"Shouldn't I just round it up to $2.5 million?"

"No," said Mike. "I like to be able to sit down with a seller and show him exactly how I arrived at the price, and why it's fair. And you never round an offer up."

"Makes sense. How do we handle the fact that the balance sheet at closing may be materially different from the one Paul put together?"

"That's why we'll predicate the offer on the delivery of a balance sheet with $570,000 of net working capital, which is the $1,252,000 in current assets minus $685,000 in total current liabilities. If the number is less, the price goes down; if it's more the price will go up."

Assets	Now	Adjustments	At Closing
Cash [A]	$100,000	<100,000>	$
Accounts Receivable	1,200,000		1,200,000
Prepaid Expenses	52,000		52,000
Total Current Assets	1,352,000		1,252,000
Fixed Assets (Net)			
Leasehold Improvements [B]	45,000	<45,000>	
Furniture Improvements [C]	70,000	<20,000>	50,000
Total Assets	$1,467,000		$1,302,000
Liabilities			
Current Liabilities			
Accounts Payable	$110,000		$110,000
Note Payable to Shareholder [D]	200,000	<200,000>	
Line of Credit	275,000		275,000
Accrued Expenses	300,000		300,000
Total Current Liabilities	885,000		685,000
Long-Term Liabilities			
Note Payable	50,000		50,000
Total Liabilities	935,000		735,000
Equity	532,000	$35,000	567,000
Total Liabilities and Equity	$1,467,000		$1,302,000

A. Seller will keep cash.
B. Adjust to zero since it is contemplated that the business will change locations.
C. The adjustment of $20,000 is necessary to show the furniture and equipment at fair market value.
D. The acquisition entity will not assume the note payable to shareholder.

"Gotcha," said Tim. "Do I need anything else for Jim Williams to put together an LOI?"

"Yes, you'll need to put in a financing contingency since we don't have a bank term sheet, right?"

"No, I was going to wait until I got a positive response to the LOI."

"I'd get on the financing tomorrow," Mike advised.

"So how do you see that working?"

"RCA's only real leverageable asset is the accounts receivable. You can assume a bank will lend eighty percent of the value of those receivables that are ninety days old or less. Let's also assume that eighty percent of the $1.2 million, or $960,000, of the accounts receivable are less than ninety days old, so they'd be eligible. Based on that, the bank should give you a senior debt facility of eighty percent of $960,000, or $768,000. You'll need to use $275,000 of this new facility to pay off the line of credit you're assuming. Add to the $768,000 the $110,000 of accounts payable and $300,000 of accrued expenses you're assuming as part of the purchase price and you've got $1,178,000 of your $2,450,000 offering price covered with bank financing and liabilities assumed.

"OK. What about the balance?"

"Have you and Sue decided what you're willing to invest?"

"We talked about it, and we were thinking $300,000."

"Good. I think with that size commitment from you the bank might match that in additional cash-flow financing. That would bring their total loan facility to $1,068,000, which is roughly four times EBITDA. Doable maybe; however, since the last $300,000 is air-ball financing—that is, as we've discussed, there's no asset to back it up—they'll want this paid off before you get your hands on much of the profits. They call it cash-flow recapture."

"That seems fair enough. So now we're up to, let's see, $1,778,000 which is comprised of: my $300,000, the new line of credit of $768,000, plus the assumed payables and accrued expenses totaling $410,000, plus the air-ball financing of $300,000. Without any additional investment, Pete will need to take back a note for, let's see, $672,000. Is that too high?"

"Yes," replied Mike. "I'd like for the seller financing portion not to exceed twenty percent or so of the purchase price, so let's say Pete will accept the note for $490,000, that means you're short by $182,000. Tim, I think it's time you talk to your mom and see if she's willing to help you out. Remember, you're also going to need some working capital to keep the business operating."

"You're right; I forgot about that. Do you think the bank would convert at least a portion of the $768,000 line of credit—say, $400,000 to long term—so we'd have less short-term debt and as a result more working capital?"

"They might, but I'd also like you to see if your mom would lend the company another, say, $182,000 for you to put into the deal."

"So don't make my mom a partner?"

"No, give her a note. You need to keep partners to a minimum. I'm sure we'll have this discussion again, but for now, trust me."

"OK, I'll ask her. Anything else we ought to cover tonight?" asked Tim.

"No. I'll tell you what, I'll send you an e-mail showing what your post-closing balance sheet will look like based on tonight's discussion. That always helps me visualize the deal."

"Thanks, Mike. You've given me a lot of great help tonight. If I get this done, would you consider joining my board of advisers?"

"Thanks, Tim, I'd be honored; just no meetings in Cincinnati in the winter except by Skype."

"Deal."

On the short walk home Tim's head was swimming. Sue saw him coming down the walk and met him at the door. "You look worn out. Was your session with Mike sensory overload?"

"Not really; it's all very logical. Just a lot to assimilate. He advised me to ask my mom for a $182,000 loan. What do you think?"

"Well . . . please don't take this as going behind your back, because I didn't. Your mom called last week and asked me how it was going and I told her you were convinced RCA was the right company but that the price was pretty steep. She said she'd be happy to help out. She's very happy for you, Tim."

"Wow, sounds like the tough part's been done already. I'll call her tomorrow, and I don't consider that going behind my back—more like you've got my back, as always." Tim added emphasis with a large hug.

"I know being the wife of an entrepreneur is going to mean I will be second fiddle for a while. Please promise that you'll let yourself have fun and enjoy the experience."

"That's really a smart observation, and you know what? I think I am old enough to understand what a privilege it will be to operate my own business, that I'll actually be able to enjoy the ride. I can't wait."

"I know you can't," said Sue. "You've been so much more fun

to be with since you've made the decision. I've got the old Tim back, and that's good."

Tim gave Sue another big hug and a rather lengthy kiss, for a weeknight.

Just before he walked out the door the next morning Tim decided to see if Mike had sent the post-closing balance sheet. Sure enough, there it was along with his note:

Tim,
I hope you find this helpful. It always helps me crystallize my thoughts. Let me know what you think.

Mike

Post-Closing Balance Sheet	
Accounts Receivable	1,200,000
Prepaid Expenses	52,000
	1,252,000
Fixed Assets	50,000
Goodwill *(difference between total price and value of tangible assets purchased)*	1,148,000
Total Assets	2,450,000
Accounts Payable	110,000
Line of Credit	368,000
Accrued Expenses	300,000
Long-Term Bank Debt *(400,000 from receivables financing plus 300,000 air-ball financing)*	700,000
Tim's Equity	300,000
Note to Seller	490,000
Note to Mom	182,000
Total Liabilities & Equity	**2,450,000**

Mike was right—this did help Tim focus, particularly on the need to pay off more than $2 million in liabilities. In a weird way it made him look more forward to the challenge, kind of like a double black diamond slope, only this time he had to ski up it!

Midmorning Tim called Jim Williams to set up a lunch meeting. Jim generously offered to meet him at the Queen City Club, where Jim was a member. Tim e-mailed Jim the summary of the offer along with Mike's balance sheet. Right at noon Tim dropped his car off with the valet and entered the side door of the 140-year-old club. He had been there a few times before and had to admit the priceless art set off by the dark wood paneling and the elegant furnishings were a tad intimidating. He waited somewhat nervously in the quiet lobby until Jim came bounding in. As he pumped Tim's hand, Jim said, "Thanks for meeting me here, Tim; I've got another meeting next door in the new Great American tower at one thirty. Great to kill two meetings with one parking lot, and it's free to boot."

"Very efficient, Jim. I like your style."

"Tell my wife—she thinks I need to update my look. I told her no way—it's Brooks Brothers suits, Countess Mara ties, Alden shoes, and no matter what, no hair gel."

"Stick to your guns. Life's too complicated to try to adhere to the latest fashion code."

"Agreed. Let's eat."

After they ordered and Jim signed the discreet slip presented by the waiter, he asked Tim, "So you've gotten to the point that an LOI is in order?"

"I think so. What should I know?"

"First, understand it's really a conditional offer and as such it's nonbinding on both sides, so I don't believe in making them too long or detailed. Otherwise, you get into negotiations that are much more appropriate for the final document, which is called the asset purchase agreement. I'll be succinct, no more than three pages or so."

"Apart from price, what are the essential elements?" asked Tim.

"How the purchase price is to be paid—so, for example, how much of it will be paid in cash at closing—liabilities that will be assumed, and the amount of the seller note. It will also cover other big items, like the working capital adjustment, due diligence requirements, timing, and most important, a provision requiring the sellers to take the business off the market while we negotiate. You'll also need a financing contingency, unless you get an OK from the bank before we send the letter."

"How long is the conditional offer usually kept open?"

"Maybe ten days, which is certainly fair with a deal this size."

Both Tim and Jim failed to resist ending their meal with the macaroon cookies, the club's specialty.

"So," asked Tim, "who should the buyer be, me or a new entity?"

"Since I'm confident you're going to make this deal happen, I'll go ahead and set up a limited liability company for you."

"Why an LLC and not an S corp?" asked Tim.

"More flexibility with an LLC. All the business's debt is part of your basis, which is the amount from which the IRS permits you to deduct any losses you might incur. This is especially likely in your early years. On the other hand, with an S corp, only the money you've contributed as paid-in capital and money you lend directly to the company establishes basis for tax losses. In addition, if you use an LLC and if for any reason you want to be a corporation later on you can do it tax-free. However, if you start off with a corporation and later decide you want to be an LLC you could incur tax."

"LLC it is, then. I want to call it H.F. Holdings."

"What's the H.F. stand for?"

"Happy Family," replied Tim.

"That's great. It's certainly my experience that an engaged entrepreneur who's engrossed in his business does make for a happy family. It may seem counterintuitive, but I believe engaged at work means happy at home."

"It's funny, Jim, even though I wasn't happy at work I really didn't think I was any different at home, but my family disagrees. They all say I'm a changed man . . . for the better."

"I guess we best get this deal done so Tim the Ogre doesn't return. When do you plan on resigning from your position at the hospital?"

"I'll wait until the LOI is accepted. I figure I'll give the hospital four weeks notice. It'll probably take that long to close."

"You're right. Taking into account the negotiation of the asset purchase agreement, getting your bank financing finalized, and completing due diligence, I think four weeks is about right."

"Jim, thanks for the info and the cookies. Both were great."

"Not often I get high praise like that. You're just angling for a return visit."

"Wouldn't mind."

"I'll get a draft of this to you by tomorrow morning."

"Thanks, Jim. I'll come to your office tomorrow afternoon to sign it, if that's OK."

"Sure, see you then."

That night Tim called Mike and told him about his lunch with Jim, closing the conversation by asking, "Are you sure I'm doing the right thing, Mike? It seems . . . well, sort of irrevocable."

"As you know, it's really not, and yes, you're doing the right thing. Marcia tells me Sue's raving about getting her old Tim back. That should tell you all that you need to know."

"You're right. I'm ready."

Tim reviewed Jim's draft (Appendix C) the next morning and forwarded it to Mike, who gave his blessing. That afternoon, he signed the letter and Jim promised it would go out in that night's mail. That night Tim thought he'd have a dream involving pushing a $2 million rock up a hill. Instead, he dreamed he was flying high over his neighborhood. He took this as a good sign.

The next morning Tim called his friend Nick Miller at Commerce Bank and e-mailed him the opening balance sheet and the LOI as they talked.

"Tim, I think I've got all I need except your personal financial statement and a forecasted income statement for your first two years."

"I'll send a personal financial statement from home tonight. I'll try to get you the forecasted statement by close of business tomorrow."

"Are you planning on making any changes?" asked Nick.

"Yes, I'm going to add a new business line, remote coding this year, and next year I am going to add another line, ICD-10 training."

"Yes, I've heard of ICD-10 from some of my other health care clients. Isn't that just a new way of coding medical records for submission to payers?"

"Yes, but if a coder's been coding under ICD-9 their whole career and now has to look at a patient record and use more than 120,000 new codes to describe the activities, it will be like requiring the coder to learn a new language. I believe it will be quite disruptive and therefore an opportunity."

"Makes sense. I look forward to receiving the rest of your information."

"Thanks, Nick, talk to you tomorrow."

That evening, sitting alone in his study, Tim recalled from instances when the hospital had acquired physicians' practices that deals tended to develop their own momentum, and once a certain pace was hit they rarely fell apart. He believed his deal was reaching that critical pace, which was both scary and exhilarating. Tim spent an hour writing down how he would grow the remote coding and ICD-10 business lines. Popping open his computer, he turned his thoughts to separate forecasted income statements for each business line. The combined new income for the first year totaled $500,000 with expenses of $400,000. He increased the combined income in year two to $1,200,000 with expenses of $900,000. This would make combined net income including RCA's existing business $400,000 in year one, increasing to $600,000 in year two.

Tim eyeballed the spreadsheet and was satisfied that the results were only slightly optimistic. According to Mike, bankers more or less expect you to slightly but not grossly overstate your case. He forwarded the spreadsheet to Nick, satisfied he could back up the numbers with a cogent plan. Tim looked at the Frank Lloyd Wright clock over his mantel and realized he had been working for four hours and it was now close to midnight. He hadn't seen time fly like that on anything business related in years. More proof, he thought, of his disengagement at work.

Early the next afternoon Tim heard from Nick. "Tim, I wasn't expecting your revised numbers until late today. You must have caught a second wind last night."

"Yeah, I've been thinking a lot about how I'd grow the business, and finally putting it all on paper was cathartic."

"Well, Tim, I have to say these numbers should support your request for a $400,000 line and $700,000 in term debt. I really only need to convince my immediate supervisor, who rarely disagrees with me. I've scheduled a meeting with him for tomorrow morning. With any luck I can get back to you tomorrow with a decision and, I would hope, a term sheet outlining the bank's commitments the following day."

"That's great, Nick. I really appreciate you making this a priority."

"Happy to do it. It's been a while since I've brought in an acquisition deal. Been a tough market. Thanks for the opportunity."

Tim hung up. Now he knew the deal had hit its critical pace. He hoped Pete wouldn't take the full ten days to respond to his

LOI. Now that the financing appeared to be in place he was starting to worry that Pete was going to respond negatively to his offer.

Tim didn't need to wait long. The next morning he got a call from Jim Williams. "Tim, I've talked to Pete Grove's counsel, Gerry Sims, and he said we should expect a counteroffer today."

"OK, so they didn't accept the offer—any idea what their counter will be?"

"The good news is they agreed to the principal terms, but would like to add a new provision which gives them the opportunity to receive more consideration if the company continues to grow, called an earn-out. Their proposed earn-out could get the total purchase price up to Pete's asking price."

"Any idea how that might be structured?"

"Yeah, Gerry said they were going to ask that half of the EBITDA you produce, over a base figure of $300,000, multiplied by five, be added to the purchase price for the next five years up to a maximum of $500,000 in total extra consideration. So, for example, if in year one EBITDA was $400,000, you'd subtract $300,000 to get to $100,000, which would be divided by two and multiplied by five, resulting in an additional payment of $250,000. So they're using a five multiple on what they consider to be earnings that you produced but that were the result of momentum they've generated, and then generously offered to split that with you."

"I haven't gotten any term sheet from the bank," said Tim, "but I know from my discussions with Mike to expect what he called a cash flow recapture provision because of the lack of collateral. I doubt I could make those payments and the proposed earn-out payments too."

"You're right. You should be receiving the bank's letter later today. I'll be cc'd on it, so I'll call you after I get it."

As soon as Tim got home he checked his e-mail to see if the counterproposal had been sent. It had been, and it read just as Jim had outlined it. He forwarded it to Mike and asked him to call that evening.

Sue saw the look on Tim's face as he left his study to eat dinner. "So how's the deal going?" He explained the earn-out wrinkle to Sue, who, being the ultimate quick study, asked, "Why should you pay extra for additional earnings you generate?"

As usual, Sue's insight was brilliant in its simple clarity.

"Good point. I suppose I was concentrating more on how to get this deal done rather than whether or not the request was fair. You're right. I don't think it's a fair request. I'm looking forward to Mike's thoughts."

Tim and Sue ate a quiet dinner, each lost in their thoughts about the deal. Just as they were finishing there was a knock on the door. They knew it was Mike, since everyone else rang the bell. Tim answered the door to see Mike grinning at him with a pencil behind each ear.

"Thought you might need some sharpened number twos to help you center your return salvo," Mike said as he gave him one of the pencils.

"You seem pretty optimistic about the counter."

"I am," Mike replied. "This deal's all but done."

Tim, Sue, and Mike sat down in Tim's study to analyze the

counteroffer. "Sue, if I had known you were going to be part of this war counsel I would have brought three pencils," Mike said with a grin.

"Not necessary, Mike; I enjoy helping with the big picture, but I'll leave the details to you guys."

After they'd studied and annotated the counteroffer with their thoughts Tim said, "So, Mike, what do you think?"

"Look, Tim, I'm not going to say it's a bluff, but it's a bluff. They responded quickly and only added a sort of desperation earn-out that no one would accept. My bet is that his advisers told him to take it but he talked them into this last-ditch attempt to get his price."

"OK, so what's next?"

"I'd tell Jim to call Gerry and tell him the original offer stands as well as the timetable. I'll bet Jim agrees with the strategy. He's been around the block enough times."

On his way out Mike asked Tim to call him on his cell if anything happened in the next few days. He was traveling to his Singer Island, Florida, home the next day to check out some work he was having done to his condo, but he wanted to be informed.

Tim's discussion with Jim went just as Mike had predicted. Jim agreed to call Gerry and inform him of the decision to stand pat.

Later that day Jim called Tim's cell. "Well, Tim, it's not always this easy, but they accepted the original offer with only one change."

"What's that?"

"They want the financing contingency removed."

"Interestingly enough, I just received the term sheet from Nick agreeing to our requested structure. As you and Mike predicted, they'd like the $700,000 piece paid off over four years, which I don't see as being a problem."

"Great. I'll redo the LOI and we'll get this thing done."

"Thanks, Jim."

Tim immediately called Mike. When he answered Tim could hear the wind and crashing waves in the background. "As usual, you were right, Mike."

"Gets kind of boring, doesn't it? Any changes to your LOI?"

"Just removing the financing contingency, but I got the term sheet today OK'ing my structure. As you predicted, they want the $700,000 term piece paid off fast, over four years."

"That shouldn't be a problem if you hit your numbers. Congrats, Tim. It looks like you bought a company. Easy, wasn't it?"

"I wouldn't say that, but it sure was fun. What about due diligence—any words of wisdom?"

"Yeah, let the lawyers and accountants do their thing, but I have my own ten-point checklist I'll send you. Based on RCA's size not all of the items on the list will be done correctly or completely, and some likely not at all. The boxes that aren't checked become your immediate strategic goals for RCA. Tim, I have no real right to feel this way, but I am very proud of you, and I'm sure your dad would be bursting with pride if he were with us."

Tim hung up the phone with a tear in his eye. Mike, as usual, was right. His dad would be proud and thrilled. After a career on the sidelines, he'd love seeing his own son not only in the entrepreneurship game but playing quarterback.

Later that day, as promised, Tim received Mike's ten-point checklist:

1. **Succession Plan**
    - Who is likely to buy your business and for how much?

2. **Growth Plan**
    - Do you have a goal that everyone in the company knows?

3. **Capital and Operating Budget**
    - Do you know what it is going to cost to execute your plan?
    - Does your bank know and agree?

4. **Short-Term Compensation Plan**
    - Is your employee compensation plan tied to the bottom line?

5. **Long-Term Compensation Plan**
    - Are your employees who add long-term value receiving value?

6. **Insurance Coverage**
    - Do you have gaps that threaten your business?

7. **IT System**
    - Is your system giving you critical information on a timely basis?

8. **Human Resources Plan**
    - Are you getting the people you need when you need them and at the right price?

9. **Retirement Plan**
    - Does your plan maximize benefits to you and your key people?

10. **Benchmarking**
    - How do you compare with your industry and where could you improve?

Tim had to admit he would not have thought of half the things on the list, and he was once again very grateful for Mike's valuable input.

Tim was tapping the steering wheel in cadence and singing along to "Layla" as he and Sue were heading to Jim Williams's office to close on RCA. During an Eric Clapton guitar solo Tim looked at Sue and asked, "You're not going to get cold feet and refuse to mortgage your future on an untested entrepreneur, are you?"

Sue turned her back to the passenger door so Tim could see the full extent of her positive body language. "Listen, I know it seems like we're taking a huge risk betting our entire net worth on the success of RCA, but I couldn't feel more confident. If I was going to get cold feet it would have been when we had that brief breakup during college."

"Yeah, that was your chance to escape. As I recall I charmed you with a handmade card asking to get back together. Cheap but effective," Tim said, grinning.

"I still have it. Not only do I love you unconditionally; I trust you unconditionally. I know you're going to excel at operating your own business."

"Thanks. I'm not sure why you're so confident, but I am relying on you to stand behind me. Since your name is on the title for the house, as well as the stock portfolio, theoretically you have more to lose than I do."

"I know," said Sue. "And although I'm confident, I do plan on applying pressure when necessary to ensure my investment reaps a handsome return.

"I may not be handsome but I will earn you a handsome return, ma'am," Tim said as they pulled into the lot next to Jim's office, a converted firehouse on the outskirts of downtown.

"I love this building. However, I always struggle with the symbolism of a business law firm with its offices in a converted firehouse," Sue said as she took in the impressive facade of the century-old structure.

"Actually, Jim's grandfather was a fireman who was stationed here for most of his career. So, not really symbolic, but there is some continuity."

As they were signing the asset purchase agreement bank notes, guarantees, and all the necessary documents to effect the transfer, Tim could tell Pete Grove had something on his mind. Finally Pete said, "Tim, could we step out into the hall for a minute?"

"Sure, Pete," Tim replied, relieved he was going to find out what Pete had been thinking about.

"Tim, I know the agreement only calls for me to assist with the transition for six months."

"Yeah, I was hoping for longer but your lawyer said you had a consulting opportunity out of town and couldn't commit to more than six months."

"Well, it turns out I have a yearlong consulting project in town that was too good to turn down, so I can be available for up to a year."

"That's great," said Tim. "What can I do to make this worth your while?"

"I'll tell you what, pick up the last year's lease payments on my Mercedes and we'll call it even."

"Deal, and thanks in advance for the help."

"Tim, with your background I'm confident you'll take RCA further than I could. It's a perfect match. I'm glad you're the new owner. As soon as I heard about your background I was confident you'd have no problem paying off your note to me," Pete said with a smile.

"Thanks, Pete. I appreciate your support, but I know I'll need plenty of guidance."

Tim couldn't stop grinning as he and Sue were driving home to get ready to host the closing dinner. "Tim, I believe that grin is even broader than the one you had on your face the day you resigned from the hospital."

"That was only my anticipatory grin; this is my kick-tail-and-take-names grin. Tomorrow's going to be the beginning of a big, new future for us. I just know it."

Sue kissed Tim's cheek and said, "We sure didn't start a life together with the thought of being big-time risk takers. Remember when we were on our honeymoon in the Cayman Islands how we both chickened out on the parasail ride?"

"One look at the boat operator and his motley crew of work-furloughed felons inspired only mortal fear, as I recall," Tim said with a wink.

"You're right, that was quite a bunch. I think the fact that we're now putting it all on the line is proof people can change."

"I guess we have. Not to sound too full of myself, but I feel like our bet on me is stacked heavily in our favor. I just know I can make RCA a huge success."

"You'd better, or we'll be the ones operating the parasail business . . . with a rowboat," Sue said with a chuckle, very pleased with her own joke.

"Look at us—suddenly I'm Warren Buffett and you think you're Jay Leno."

Being an accountant at heart, Tim hosted a closing dinner that was festive if somewhat down-market, in that the juicy steaks and cabernet were being served in his dining room rather than Jeff Ruby's Precinct steak house. No one seemed to care. Paul and Jim agreed Tim would not only be successful but would also be a lucrative new client. This, of course, was discussed out of Tim's earshot, but after their loud guffaws they were forced to let him in on the joke. Tim was appreciative of their keen interest in his success, but he also hoped the rather austere affair would set the tone that he was going to be watching his pennies. Nick Miller pulled him aside and complimented him not only on a successful acquisition but also for setting a homey and convivial tone for the evening, and promised the bank's full support.

Just before dessert Mike stood up and raised his glass of champagne. "Tim, little did I know when we moved here a few years ago that I would strike up one of the most rewarding relationships of my business career. Watching you in action these past few months has convinced me you are going to succeed in a big way, and not just because you're a good listener to me and all your advisers." This last comment elicited loud, partially champagne-fueled laughter.

When the laughter subsided Tim stood up and raised his own glass. "You know what, Mike, you're right. I have listened to all of you and as a result, you've helped me make what I believe will be a life-changing move. I am so grateful to all of you but especially to you, Mike. You took a fatherly interest in my family and me and provided the kind of real-world advice that I frankly plan on tapping for as long as it's provided—that is, so long as the price is right."

Laughing loudly, Mike responded, "So far, Tim, you've gotten the neighborly discount, which will continue until you get to the point where you're embarrassed not to share some of your newfound wealth."

That night Tim had a hard time falling asleep. He interrupted Sue's reading, saying, "I hope it's not just not knowing what I don't know, but I am feeling very confident that RCA is really going to work out. I've got a strong team of advisers who I believe will help me avoid the big mistakes, and I know my skills can really be utilized growing RCA. Thanks for your belief in me. You've really made this fun and easy."

"Tim, it will be great if RCA is a roaring success, but that's not nearly as important to me as you being fulfilled in your business life. I can tell you're happy and engaged, and that means everything to me."

Tim was now able to fall asleep realizing that while buying RCA may have been a good decision, marrying Sue was clearly the best decision he'd ever made.

Chapter Six

PARTNERING
(Eight Months Later)

Tim took the time on the flight to West Palm for his meeting with Mike to write down his reflections on his first six months in business as well as his questions for Mike. Business had been great. RCA had made just over $300,000 in its first two quarters, and Tim believed they'd hit $600,000 or more for the first year. The remote-coding business had really taken off, thanks to Linda Gordon. Not long after the closing Linda had approached Tim and asked if she could join RCA specifically to champion the remote-coding business line. Tim had finally understood her conspiratorial wink at the Caffs & Laffs coffee shop months earlier. It had not been a tough decision, since Linda agreed to defer part of her low base salary of $50,000 until the remote-coding business took off. However, as a result of her negotiations, if she was able to hit her budget, which now looked likely, she'd be due well over $100,000 for her first year. This sizable outflow was not much of a worry to Tim, since the company's projected results could easily fund this, the bank debt, and, thank God, some distributions for him.

Mike saw Tim walking toward him in the baggage claim area before Tim saw him. He had to admit Tim seemed to be carrying himself with more authority and confidence since buying RCA.

Of course, the Ferragamo loafers and custom shirt and blazer didn't hurt. When they met they hugged and Mike pushed Tim back to arm's length. "You look . . . prosperous. I see you've upgraded your wardrobe from your hospital days."

"It was easy to stand out when everybody else was in scrubs. Now that I can hang out in Palm Beach with a wealthy friend, I hope to be able to at least look the part."

Shaking his head, Mike responded, "I must admit I miss our back-fence repartee when I'm down here. Since you look so sharp, I'll take you to the Breakers for lunch and the initial debriefing. Then we'll recreate Mike Collins–style this afternoon."

"So what's that, a full Olympic triathlon?" Tim said somewhat kiddingly.

"Close, actually. We're going to bike to Jupiter Beach. I'll buy you a lemonade at the Lazy Loggerhead."

"Mike, the Lazy Loggerhead is ten miles up the beach from your condo. A twenty-mile bike ride might require a nap before dinner."

"That's OK. I'll swim my mile while you nap. It's important to be in top physical condition if you're going to maintain the energy necessary to be a high-achieving executive," Mike said as he stowed Tim's luggage in the trunk of his Maserati Quattroporte.

As he did this, Tim was sizing him up. Mike looked tan and fit after a season in Florida, and Tim had to admit, since he had acquired RCA he was having a hard time knowing when to stop working. He had just been so engaged he hadn't found the time to exercise regularly. Getting this in balance was one of the many things he wanted to discuss with Mike.

Over a fantastic lunch of club sandwiches and sinful (mortal variety) truffle french fries at the Breakers, Tim gave Mike the State of the Union.

"After that report I'd say it's time you bought," Mike said with some seriousness.

"Happy to, Mike. It's not exactly an even trade for our lunch at Aglamesis last year, but then again I'd say your guidance has been more than worth the difference."

As Mike pored over RCA's financial statements, Tim stared out the Seafood Bar's open windows, taking in the immaculately maintained grounds of the Breakers and the peaceful lapping of the ocean against the seawall. His reverie was broken with Mike's loud exclamation. "Wow, Tim, your numbers are great! However, you might need a little more room on your line of credit if your growth continues."

"Why is that?" Tim asked, as though a parent had found fault with an "A" paper.

"Well, as you grow your sales, your accounts receivable increase, and since your cost of sales is mostly wages, which you must pay every two weeks, it's pretty easy for your line of credit to get strained."

"You're right. I really can't stretch out my payables since most of my expenses are payroll related, as you pointed out. And although our hospital clients are not credit risks, they don't pay for forty-five days or so, causing a little imbalance in my cash flow."

"High-class problem," Mike said with a proud look.

"Thanks for inviting me down for a long weekend, Mike. I could use a little R and R, along with the advice."

"You look a little ragged. Nothing a few days in the sun won't cure, though. Remember, it won't all be R and R. This is your first quasi–board of advisers meeting."

"I wouldn't call it quasi just because it's the two of us."

"It's quasi because I'm not going to insist on my usual board fee . . . except I will let you buy dinner one night. I'll pick up lunch, though. The Breakers, I believe, was named for its effect on most people's budgets."

"But worth it," Tim said as he took a moment to take in the details of the Seafood Bar.

"I think so. Let's go; we've wasted enough of this great weather in here. Gotta get you exposed to some of the most expensive vitamin D on the planet," Mike said, pushing his chair away from the table.

As promised, Mike wore Tim out with the twenty-mile bike ride. That night Mike, Marcia, and Tim had dinner at Seasons 52. After dinner the three of them moved outside to the restaurant patio for an after-dinner drink. "I can see why the two of you enjoy this area so much," Tim said as they watched the yachts glide by on the intercoastal, the water shimmering with their running lights.

"Sure beats snow blowers and window scrapers. I hope never to use either again," said Mike.

"Spoken like a true snowbird," Marcia said to her husband as she flagged down a waiter, who took their after-dinner drink order.

"I've got no problem with being a snowbird. It just seems like the older you get the less tolerable winter is."

Giving Tim an appraising look, Marcia said, "Sue says you're knocking it out of the park."

"She may be overstating it slightly, but your husband uttered such a loud 'WOW' at the Breakers today after he saw my numbers that one of the old waiters spilled a Bloody Mary; looked like a scene from *Scarface*."

"Marcia, that is full-out hyperbole. Seems being an entrepreneur has given Tim a certain license with the truth. Hope he uses it only for fun and not with his banker," Mike said, shaking the ice in his drink for emphasis.

After Tim paid out and they waited for the valet to bring the car, Mike said, "OK, Tim, fun's over. Tomorrow we spend a day going over your plans to accomplish the open items on my 360 checklist plus whatever other issues you consider pressing. And, by the way, thanks for dinner."

Marcia chimed in, "Yes, Tim, thanks; however, as you're our guest this weekend I'd prefer if Mike paid."

"My pleasure, Marcia. It really is the least I could do. Plus, Sue told me to be on my best behavior so you don't cancel your girls' weekend down here next month."

"No chance of that," said Mike. "It's all Marcia's been talking about. Based on my intelligence it's going to be full-tilt, scorched-earth shopping from Worth Avenue to the outlet malls." He gave Marcia a squeeze.

At eight the next morning Tim and Mike met in Mike's condominium's meeting room, which overlooked a lengthy stretch of the beach. As promised, Mike forced Tim to run all the traps. Each of the ten-part 360 checklist was worked through in exhausting detail. Around three p.m. Mike pronounced the session a success and suggested a run before dinner. Tim agreed; however, Mike had a feeling there was something else on his mind.

"Mike, there's one more item we need to discuss. Although your ten-point list doesn't mention it directly, I guess it may fall under HR."

From Tim's tone Mike knew he was about to find out why Tim had seemed somewhat distracted throughout their meeting, notwithstanding his excellent progress with RCA. "So, Tim, you sound serious—what's up?"

Tim took a few seconds to collect his thoughts and said, "I mentioned to you that Linda Gordon has really done a fantastic job not only getting the remote-coding business off the ground but also growing it into a very profitable business line with probably the greatest potential for future growth."

Sensing Tim's somewhat amped-up emotions, Mike responded calmly, "OK, that sounds good so far. I know from our conversation earlier today that you're satisfied that her compensation plan is fair, particularly since she agreed to defer part of her base."

"No, that part's working out fine. The problem, if you'd call it that, is she wants to buy into the company now."

Now it was Mike collecting his thoughts, giving Tim a sympathetic slow nod of his head. He finally responded, "I'd call it a problem. How did it come up?"

"Last week we had lunch together and she said there were a couple of matters she wanted to discuss. I thought she just wanted to take a bow or two for remote coding's great performance, which she did. However, she quickly segued into the partnership track she'd abandoned at her CPA firm, her willingness to defer part of her pay, and that she would like to buy into the company." Tim's description of the lunch had come out rather staccato and flat, like maybe Sue had heard it a time or ten already.

"You don't sound too happy about it, Tim. Did the topic come up at all when you hired her?"

"Only in the most general way . . . like, 'If I prove myself I may want the chance to be an owner someday.' My response, as I recall, was somewhat positive but totally noncommittal. Frankly I was caught flat-footed." Even now Tim looked a bit flummoxed.

"So what was your response?"

"I told her I was meeting with you the following week and I'd talk to her about it when I got back."

"First meeting and I'm already cast as the bad guy, eh?"

"More like the voice of reason, I hope," Tim said with some resignation.

"That's the problem when you've obviously got something good going—people want in. In my experience taking on a partner at the wrong time or for the wrong reason, or even worse, both, is one of the most common and biggest mistakes a business owner can make. It was unfair of her to put you in that position. You'll learn to get agendas ahead of time for these so-called casual lunches. Unfortunately most employees view lunch with the boss as open season for lobbying for their causes," Mike said, shaking his head.

"So what do I say?"

"For now tell her that the board has said that it's too early to decide if she should have the right to buy in. By the way, just out of curiosity, did she mention a price?"

"She wanted to pay $90,000 for twenty-five percent of the company equity, a twenty percent premium over my original equity in the deal." Tim's tone told Mike he was somewhat embarrassed by his predicament.

"Not shy, anyway," Mike said, trying to break the tense mood. "Tim, I didn't think we'd need to cover this yet or I'd have already given you my well-established philosophy on partners. If you would have told me that she was interested in an equity stake at the time you hired her I'd have suggested you tell her that you consider such a decision to be premature and she shouldn't base her decision to join the company on the opportunity to be an owner."

"Yeah, I wish I could have thought that fast," Tim said wistfully.

"So obviously you don't feel right about selling her an interest now?"

Tim responded, "No, I really don't. I've just gotten started and don't really need the money, at least not yet. It just doesn't feel right."

"Your gut is right, Tim; it's too early. I've known many people with great ideas who just sort of brought a friend along for the ride and unfortunately made the friend a partner. Most of them were just a little scared of being on their own. As an entrepreneur, I know those early days can feel like dog years; however, the entrepreneurs who decided to go it alone were happier later. Nothing's worse than having a partner who hasn't measured up pocket part of what, you know in your heart, are your profits."

In the middle of Mike's sermon he had gotten up and was now pacing the room. Finally he quit pacing and was staring out at the beach.

"Sounds like you've had some experience with this."

Snapping out of his trance, Mike responded, "I learned a very expensive lesson in one of my earliest deals. The truth is business and friendship are tough to mix successfully. As a practicing lawyer I presided over almost as many partnership funerals as I did successful business partnerships. So yeah, I'm pretty jaded. I've since learned that it's usually better to preserve a friendship by forgoing a partnership, even if there's some tough love involved. You need to consider your company's equity as your most valuable asset. It's rarely a good idea to trade an unknown like the value of your equity for a known like money or a skill. It's not like *Let's Make a Deal*, when you must trade for what's behind door number two."

"You know what, Mike? You've hit the nail on the head. Even without the benefit of your advice I didn't feel like the discussion was timely or appropriate."

"Since you didn't say anything to the contrary, I assume Linda's skill set is not so unique that it couldn't be purchased for cash alone."

"She's smart, motivated, organized, and a hard worker, but no, she's really just executing my remote-coding business plan. I'll have to admit, she's doing it perfectly and has an intuitive sense, particularly when it comes to recruiting the new coders, but I wouldn't say that what she's doing is so unique that someone else couldn't do it."

Mike was again staring out the window and began his response before turning his head. "Also, there's more than an even chance you'll need to raise money sometime in the future. And it's likely to require giving up some equity."

Tim responded, "That's probably true. I've already run into a few companies that look rather ripe, but they're certainly too big for me to consider buying now. I don't have the capital or the bench strength."

"Exactly. Chances are, particularly with the disruption in the marketplace caused by ICD-10, there will be some smaller coding companies that won't have the resources to train their coders and as a result would rather sell and let a buyer bring their folks up to speed."

"Still wish I'd have had all these thoughts organized when I met with Linda."

"That's what boards are for, Tim. One of a board's key roles is to help you avoid the big mistakes, and even though you may not have handled Linda's request artfully, you didn't make a mistake."

"You're right; it's just a little awkward."

"Awkward's better than wrong," said Mike. "You'll get over it, and I think Linda will too if you handle it properly. I suppose Linda signed an employment contract with a noncompete clause."

"She did, but she was a tough negotiator and it ended up being pretty weak. That's another reason I'm worried."

"I wouldn't worry too much about that. You know, my first ten years as a business owner I worried about my employees becoming competitors. Now I wish they would have. I'd have eaten their lunch."

"Tough talk," said Tim.

"Yeah, well, I pretty much believe entrepreneurs are entrepreneurs and employees, no matter how talented, are employees. So I wouldn't include not wanting Linda as a competitor as a good reason to allow her to buy in."

That evening they grilled on Mike and Marcia's back porch. Mike's pairing of grouper with a crisp pinot grigio was perfect. The view from their ten-story balcony was stunning, and since it was a clear night they were able to see all the way to the Breakers. After dinner Mike went inside, grabbed two cigars from his humidor, and said to Marcia, "Tim and I are going to conclude our partnership discussion out here on the porch. You're invited to stay if you can tolerate the smoke."

"I'll pass," Marcia replied. "Tim, I hope Mike's not been too negative about partners. I recall at least two who were fine people, hard workers and they added a lot of value," she said in a semi-scolding tone.

"Yeah, two out of what . . . ten? I'd say that's about average."

"Mike, I like what you said this morning about avoiding the big mistakes," said Tim. "The managing partner of my old CPA firm used to say that business was like weekend tennis: Whoever makes the fewest mistakes wins."

"Smart man; I'll use that," Mike said as he lit his cigar. "Tim, I would like to give you some more insight into partners. You know, I'm not really against the idea—I'm all for it when it's appropriate."

"So, based on our earlier conversation, you'd say it's only worth it if the potential partner has some unique skill that he or she would provide only in exchange for equity?"

"Yes, but I'd include having his or her own book of business in the definition of unique skills."

"In other words, a rainmaker?"

"Yes," Mike replied. "One that's already made rain for you or has a business they can merge into yours. Even then you need to make sure your personalities mesh. Business partnerships, unlike marriages that have children to hold them together, are really all about the money."

Tim could tell Mike was on a roll, because he was using his cigar alternately like a conductor's baton and a fencing foil. He now knew from experience that he was about to get Mike unplugged. He had to admit when Mike was in his element, like this, his freewheeling advice was not only helpful; it was darn entertaining.

"Tim, even though the sole purpose of a business partnership is the advancement of a business enterprise, personalities always play a role and, as you know, different personalities have different outlooks on how the advancement should take place, and it's often significantly different."

"Even though I was never a partner at my CPA firm, I could see that dynamic play out with the partners. If I didn't like the response to a request I'd forum-shop with different partners until I found an ally."

"You get it, then. Here's the deal." Mike was again parrying with his Macanudo. "Partnerships seem to work best when the enterprise is only doing pretty good. If it's doing really good, then there's probably more money to divvy up than the partners expected. I know, a high-class problem, but still a problem. Inevitably one of the partners believes—and he's usually right—that his contribution to the success of the organization is disproportionate to his ownership. Of course, if this is true the converse is also true and his partner is not pulling his weight. As you can imagine, this kind of friction is usually incendiary."

"I can tell you've had some real-world experience here."

"Darn right, and it was an expensive lesson." Mike paused for a second. "Funny, there's also likely to be problems with partnerships when the business does poorly."

"I suppose then it's a blame game," Tim said, gaining more understanding of the partnership dynamic.

"Right. And neither partner sees it as a case of proportional mutual fault. As you'd expect, recriminations generally follow. So unless you plan on running just a so-so business, you've just got to be very, very careful."

"So when it's time—and I'm sure you'll let me know when it is—what should I be looking for?"

"Four things," said Mike.

"Let me have 'em."

Mike was now hitting his stride. "First thing, make sure your partner has a skill that complements yours. If you're too much alike, all you'll do is compete. Doesn't work.

"Next, as I've already mentioned, but it's so important I'll make you listen to it twice: Make sure your partner has a skill that can't be purchased with some currency cheaper than your company's valuable equity. And even if the skill is hard to find, it still may be less unique than yours, so make sure you account for that when you decide on the equity split."

"All that makes sense. What's number three?" asked Tim.

"Don't pick someone who is too rich or too poor. If he's too poor, failure doesn't hurt as much, his bank guarantee is not as valuable, and he will be unable to answer a capital call if the business should need money later. On the other hand, if your partner's too rich, success is likely not as important as it is to you, and neither is the specter of paying back company loans with personal funds in the event of a business reversal."

"OK, what's number four?"

"Make sure you choose a partner who shares your personal values. You're not going to be able to change your partner's values after you're in business together. This includes not only work-life effectiveness but more important, business and personal ethics. You should be proud of your association personally as well as professionally."

Tim, having absorbed Mike's words, responded, "That's really a well-thought-out approach to partner selection, Mike. Have you had any associations that measured up?"

"In my first few deals, no; later, yes. But honestly, I generally go it alone now or take a smaller piece in an existing business that needs capital and some guidance. I suppose I'm so passionate about it because it's such an avoidable problem if it's approached with business logic and not a false sense of what I would call communalism. After eight months in business, you know now that being an entrepreneur is tough and so is being a partner. Combining the two makes it that much harder to operate a business. It's not that one and one can never equal three—it can. It's just been my experience that the more common sum is less than two. That's enough of this serious stuff—let's talk cars."

On the flight home Tim turned his notes from the board meeting with Mike to a new action plan for RCA's next twelve months. Just as he and Mike had discussed at Aglamesis when Mike posed the ten entrepreneurial questions, it was now obvious that he had to be able to live with significant uncertainty. He now knew that no matter how much he planned, nothing ever worked out perfectly, and matters like Linda's request would always come up and temporarily derail his plans. He also believed he was getting the big picture, which was that following good advice and making sure business issues were always analyzed first from a hyper-logical perspective would prevent that irrevocable big mistake.

Chapter Seven

FAMILY BUSINESS
(Three Years Later)

Seth held the stock of his Beretta 12 gauge tight to his cheek as he stood at the last skeet station. After tracing the arc of the last bird with his barrel, he yelled, "Pull," to the trapper. When the bird was directly overhead, Seth pulled the trigger, resulting in a black smudge of airborne dust and a groan from his father. Seth popped open his over-and-under, caught the ejected shell, and blew the smoke coming from the barrel directly and defiantly at his father. "That's twenty-one to twenty; I win. I guess you're going to spring for cheeseburgers at the Main Street Café."

"That was the deal," Tim said, feigning disappointment. In reality he was very proud not only that Seth had become a pretty good shot but also that he was becoming a pretty good business-man. Since graduating from the University of Dayton two years before, he had moved rapidly up the ranks at Commerce Bank. Tim could tell from the increasingly sophisticated content of their nightly dinner discussions that Seth was more than han-dling the steep learning curve. Tim would have to admit that even he was learning a thing or two about the banker's mental-ity from his nightly discussions with Seth. Seth reminded him so much of his own father as he carefully explained the bank's role in tricky lending situations and complicated multiparty deals. Seth not only understood how the risk and reward in each deal was analyzed; he understood each borrower's business and how important access to capital was for growing that business. In short, although Tim knew he was biased, he'd say that Seth was a natural.

After Seth placed his usual order of two cheeseburgers through the garden, a bowl of chili, and a bottle of Bud, Tim looked up at the waitress and said, "Cut that order in half for me, except for the Bud. I think I can handle all twelve ounces."

Seth was unusually quiet as they ate. Finally, he gave Tim a serious look and said, "Dad, I've been trying to find the right time to bring this up. Honestly, I really didn't think it would be this awkward."

"Seth, is something wrong?" Tim asked, fearing his son was facing a truly serious issue.

"I wouldn't say something's wrong. I'm just having second thoughts about a career in banking. I'm learning a lot, and based on the increasingly complex deals I've been asked to work on, I know that I am well thought of. I just . . . I don't really see a job above mine that looks all that interesting. I know there is more to learn, but it seems like the next level is more about how to handle customers and how to mine for new business. I know that's important, but I have to admit that the idea of busting it so that the bank can make more money only to have so little of it trickle down to me doesn't provide a lot of incentive."

Tim was relieved that Seth's problem was business related and not something more serious. Although he'd been half-expecting a conversation like this, he'd thought it wouldn't come for a few more years. Seth was obviously being strongly influenced by Tim's frequent stories of RCA's successes as well as the direct impact of those successes on the family's bottom line.

"Well, Seth, I understand your frustration, but as my dad said, you need to eat your peck of dirt before you die."

"Yeah, Dad, you've told me that before and I get it; it's just that I feel I could be learning faster and adding value more quickly at a job where I was a little closer to the action."

"Seth, I'd look at it this way: You're still learning a lot, and, by the way, the customer service stuff you will be learning at the next level is even more important than the technical stuff you've learned so far. In addition, you're making good money, and although you may not see the perfect job above you, the fact that the bank is giving you more and more responsibility is a great sign. You're only twenty-three, so the advice that I'm about to give you—advice I got from my dad twenty years ago—is quite apropos."

"OK, Dad, I know this will be good. Did Grandpa ever say anything that wasn't profound?"

"Sure, but it was usually during a traffic jam or just after his team lost a critical game," Tim said with a smile.

"I guess you inherited that, huh, Dad?" Seth said with that knowing smirk sons love using on dads when they catch them in something.

"Guilty as charged. Anyway, Grandpa said the most important thing about your early years is to build a strong knowledge base by continually challenging yourself to learn critical business skills. Over time, you'll refine that knowledge through extensive experience into sound business judgment. As he put it, the guys who were making the big bucks were the guys who had great judgment. Unfortunately, in a large organization like Commerce, there is no shortcut to being one of the big guys."

"I agree completely. It's just that it's a little frustrating at times."

"I know. Look at it this way. Between now and age thirty-five you're likely to spend most of your earnings on non-appreciating assets. What you're earning is basically only determining your short-term lifestyle. The real key is having high-value skills at age thirty-five so you can maximize earnings during your critical earning years of thirty-five to sixty-five."

"Makes sense, Dad. I guess seeing the fun you're having has made me a little impatient."

"Kind of reminds me of how you shot at your first skeet outings. You'd try to shoot the bird as soon as it left the house. While your reflexes were impressive and you occasionally had a spectacular shot, you soon learned that exercising a little patience and keeping your barrel moving along the arc of the bird's flight was far more effective."

"Yeah, effective enough to beat you two of three," Seth said as he handed Tim the check.

In the car on the way home, Seth was back to normal, talking about his girlfriend, the Bengals, and his ongoing quest to find just the right two-family near Hyde Park Square.

A couple of weeks later Tim was driving to work when he noticed an envelope sticking out of the inside breast pocket of his suit coat on the seat of his car. He pulled it out and saw that there was only one word on the envelope: "Dad." Kim always called him Pop, so he knew it was from Seth. Since he was only a few blocks from work he decided he could wait to open the envelope. Once he hit the door, his assistant, Meggie, saw him and pointed to the phone in her hand as she was speaking, indicating he had a call. Before Tim could come up for air, he looked at his watch and saw it was almost noon. He had promised to meet Mike for lunch at Jean-Robert's Table, a new casual French restaurant downtown that Mike favored. As he put on his coat he felt Seth's envelope. Amazed that he had forgotten all about it, he quickly opened it, hoping that it didn't contain some time-sensitive request that he had already blown. Inside was a note:

Dad,

After our lunch I did a lot of thinking about our conversation, particularly the part about learning business skills to make myself more valuable. I have concluded that the best way for me to do this, at a pace that would satisfy me, would be working for you. Not to swell your head, Dad, but what I hear from you at dinner every night is far more insightful and valuable than what I'm learning at the bank.

I know your CFO is looking for an assistant. I'd like you to add my enclosed résumé to the stack. I hope that it gains me an interview for the job. Based on the Monster posting I'd say my skills fit the job description pretty closely.

Dad, I've always prized our special relationship and think working together would only strengthen our bond. I'd be very proud to join your great team.

Love,

Seth

Tim wiped the tears from his eyes as he made his way toward the lobby. Although this development didn't really come as a shock, particularly after their lunch, it did have Tim swaying on his pins a bit. Seth was right; the assistant CFO position would be a great place for him to obtain some of those valuable business skills they had discussed.

It was serendipitous that he had this lunch with Mike scheduled, since he would be very interested in Mike's take on the matter. Tim had been chatting with Mary Lou, the maître d', for only a minute when Mike walked into the restaurant, kissed Mary Lou on both cheeks, and gave Tim his patented bear hug. "Good to see you, Tim. Love this place—food's great and the atmosphere is just the right mix of conviviality and formality."

"Glad we had this lunch set up, Mike. I need a healthy dose of your insight on what I've got in my pocket."

"Not a love note from your bank telling you it's time to find a new lender, I hope," Mike said with a smile, knowing that with RCA's numbers any bank in town would be proud to have the company as a customer.

"No, far more complicated than that," Tim said as he handed Mike Seth's letter and résumé.

After they were seated, Mike read the letter, occasionally glancing up at Tim with a look that Tim would later describe as sweet when he discussed their lunch with Sue.

"So the time has come to decide if RCA is going to be a family business?" Mike said with a grin.

"I guess so. It was always a dream, but I must admit I'm not altogether prepared to respond to Seth's request," Tim said, shrugging his shoulders and arching his eyebrows at a bemused Mike.

"You're right to consider this to be an extremely important decision. Bringing a family member aboard can really change the company dynamic. Often the wrong family hire can destroy the belief that the company is a meritocracy. Morale can sink fast if your team believes their upside is limited by their bloodline."

"Strong words, Mike. As usual, it sounds like you've got a story or two."

"Make that a story or eighteen."

"Eighteen?"

"Yeah, I added it up once. During my thirty years or so in business I have hired fifteen nieces and nephews and all three of my children, honestly with almost universally positive results." Mike paused and let out a little chuckle. "You know, I did have one nephew who occasionally showed up in the morning in the same clothes he'd had on the day before and there were some rumors of him snoozing in the file room."

"Doesn't sound like that was so positive."

"Sort of the exception that proves the rule, I guess. The jobs were mostly summer positions where neither my relatives nor I were making a long-term commitment. So it was a much easier call."

"I know your son Pat is the CEO of See and Be Seen. By the way, that has to be the best name out there for a chain of high-end optical shops."

"Marcia's idea, of course," Mike said proudly. "Pat was a pre-med major at Vanderbilt and when he got out he decided business looked like more fun than medicine. By that time I had ten stores around Nashville and was doing pretty well, and Pat asked if he could work with me."

"I thought Pat was an optometrist."

"That's part of the rest of the story. I told him if he wanted to work for me he had to add something I didn't already have. So he went to optometry school, graduated, and got a job with one of the large national eyeglass chains."

"I didn't know that. So he learned the big chain's MO and helped you grow See and Be Seen?"

"I'd say his excellent experience with the national chain was one of the biggest reasons we were able to grow so quickly and remain profitable. Not every family hire needs to measure up to that standard to be successful; however, I think you need to keep that standard top of mind when you make the call."

"Food for thought." As if on cue their waiter arrived with their lunches.

"Tim, I think this would be an excellent agenda item for next week's board meeting. Do you feel comfortable seeking the rest of the board's insights on this?"

"Definitely. I really feel like we've got a cohesive group at RCA and some real momentum. I'd hate to jeopardize that in any way."

Tim paid the check, a more common occurrence now that he had, according to Mike, earned the right to buy. As they were walking out of the restaurant, he turned toward Mike and said, "Thanks for your insight. This is going to be a tricky one, isn't it?"

"A little. I'll share more of my thoughts at the meeting. I am confident you'll make the right call."

"That makes one of us," Tim said as they waited for the valet to bring Mike's car around. The valet was clearly thrilled not only with the $20 tip Mike handed him but also for the chance to drive a Cobra, if only for a half block.

"No Ducati today?" Tim asked.

"No, I didn't think that my leathers would be proper attire, so I took the Cobra. It's really just a four-wheeled motorcycle," Mike said, grinning like a sixteen-year-old in his first jalopy. "See you next week, Tim." With that Mike sped off, the roar of the Cobra's barely muffled side pipes echoing off the glass facades of the downtown buildings.

Watching him drive off, Tim just shook his head and muttered to himself, "Someday."

RCA's board, in addition to Mike and Tim, included Rick Shoemaker, the retired CEO of St. Jude's, a large local hospital, and Joe Dobson, the retired managing partner of the CPA firm where Tim had begun his career. Both added an amazing amount of insight, the kind you can get from not only being able to say, "been there, done that," but also from being required to live with some pretty significant mistakes. Tim was beginning to realize how much he could learn from others' mistakes and how much more successful a business could be if he simply avoided the big mistakes others have made.

The board convened in one of the small private conference rooms at the Queen City Club. As usual, the meeting started with Stan Tankersly, RCA's CFO, presenting the financial update. The company was on track to achieve sales of $10 million and net income of more than $1 million. Both numbers would be firsts for the company and represented milestones that Tim was particularly proud of. Shaking his head and wearing a big smile, Joe said, "Congratulations on great results, Stan. I know those figures represent more than just abstract goals; they also represent a lot of hard work. Paying strict attention to keeping your margins up on all your product lines while keeping tight reins on your SG & A expenses is quite a balancing act."

Stan responded, "Thanks, Joe, you're right. It has been a lot of hard work, particularly maintaining our margins on our older, less proprietary product lines where we have to compete with smaller players with less overhead, and where our ability to reduce cost through our technology is limited. As a result, we've had to rely on superior service to keep our prices up and efficient execution to keep costs down. It sometimes feels like we're spinning a lot of plates on the ends of sticks like the guy on the old Ed Sullivan Show, and often several of the plates get wobbly at the same time." The old-time reference elicited guffaws from all three of the outside board members.

"Apt analogy, Stan. Tim, did you ever see that guy?" asked Rick.

"Stan has used that analogy so often I finally looked it up on YouTube. It really does present the appropriate visual for keeping this company on track."

Having finished his report, Stan got up to leave. Mike stopped him. "Stan, I know this isn't on the agenda, but Tim shared your need for an assistant CFO with me. Can you give the board a little flavor of what you think the correct candidate should look like? Maybe we can help."

"Well, I find I'm spending so much time making sure the sales folks aren't giving our services away that I'm unable to keep track of our other key performance indicators. So I guess margin oversight is the most important area for the new hire to be able to handle. I'd also like someone to be the liaison with our second bank. You know, for smaller CAPX term loans . . . that sort of thing. I really don't need someone who's all that experienced, just smart, energetic, and willing to learn. It wouldn't hurt if they had a little presence, so in a pinch they could handle the margin discussions with the sales team, as well handling the bank, without much backup."

Mike, seated closest to Stan, shook his hand and said, "Thanks, Stan, that's really helpful. Look forward to seeing you at our next meeting."

Once Stan was out of the room Mike said, "Tim, in order for Rick and Joe not to be caught flat-footed I spoke to both of them about Seth's request. I hope you don't mind."

"Not at all. I hope Stan's description of the position I'm considering for Seth was helpful. I've also brought copies of his résumé for you." Tim passed out Seth's résumé and gave the members a few minutes to digest it.

Joe led off. "Great grades, good but not great experience with the bank. Don't know Seth well, but from the times we've been together I know he has the presence part with a capital P."

"Thanks, Joe," Tim said. "He is a natural with people and his experience as a college lacrosse player, including team captain, has really helped him with his confidence and his leadership abilities.

"You know," Tim continued, "in advising dozens of family businesses during my time in the CPA business, I've noticed, when it's done right, each succeeding generation can actually become stronger managers. Growing up around the business, they're exposed to every aspect because of their unlimited access to the owner. Even before they're in the business they've vicariously worn all the hats the owner has through dinner table discussions. If they've paid strict attention—and I assume Seth has or we wouldn't be having this conversation—they'd likely add a lot of value quickly."

Nodding his head, Rick added, "You know, my dad had a successful metal plating company. I used to work there summers during high school and college. Hated it. And as a result didn't learn much. My brother, Brian, on the other hand, loved it, learned every aspect of the business, and saw the company's success as a mission. When Brian joined the company, right after college, Dad said he set such a high standard that he successfully raised the bar for everyone in the organization."

"Of course, the converse is also true," added Joe. "I know we've often discussed the age-old problem of small businesses hiring too fast and firing too slow. Usually it's even more acute when family is involved. Many times I've seen family members take advantage of their status, believing a relative would not fire them, and perform accordingly. Someone like that can wipe out the esprit de corps overnight. I recall one client who had hired two of his chronically unemployed nephews. He soon found out why they couldn't hold a job. I had to step in and tell him they needed to be ejected fast and remind him that he was running a for-profit business for his family, not a halfway house for his relatives.

The group had pushed their chairs back, realizing that Joe was on a roll. He continued, "Our practice was almost one hundred percent family owned businesses, so we probably saw it all. My partner Ed, who was quite the comedian, had a theory about family businesses that he called cell biology."

Tim looked at Joe quizzically and said, "Cell biology? I don't get it."

"Yes, according to Ed some relatives, particularly cousins, believe that a family business is a means of money being transferred diffusion-like from areas of higher concentration—that is, the business owner—to areas of lesser concentration; that is, themselves.

"I've seen that syndrome a number of times, Joe, but I've never heard it called cell biology. That's perfect," Mike said as he jotted the term on his notepad.

"OK, Mike, we need you to perform your usual oracle-like function and sum this up for us," Tim said, looking more confused than informed.

"OK," Mike said as he stood up and started to pace, the small room cramping his flamboyant style—but not his critical thinking, Tim noticed. "Since I know Seth better than Joe or Rick, and unlike Tim, I can be unbiased, I'd say on the 'it' level—that is, does Seth have 'it,' he does! Not only have I seen him paying rapt attention to Tim as he laid out a business problem; he's actually been able, especially since his stint with the bank, to add keen insight, particularly when it comes to financial issues. Furthermore—sorry, Tim—like his mom he's a great observer of people and has shown the ability to suss out some of Tim's tougher personnel issues." Mike had stopped pacing and was now staring at the Ohio River out the south-facing window.

Joe took advantage of Mike's pause to add, "So you're saying Seth has the intangible part covered. Now we have to determine if what he's learned from Tim and his time with the bank will allow him to do that part of Stan's job that's bogging him down. I'd say yes. If he was going to have to take a role as a controller with more debit and credit responsibilities, then I'd say he needs more accounting seasoning, but as an assistant controller, where he's being asked to be more evaluative of the numbers and to take action to improve them, I'd say he's ready."

Rick had been listening intently, and finally after several taps of his Montblanc on his legal pad, which got everyone's attention, he added, "My only concern is that last part, Joe. Sometimes it's tough for people who are asked to analyze the numbers to also have the skills to manage the operations the numbers represent. It really is two different skill sets. It's not that Seth couldn't do it; however, it's clearly not something he's been asked to do at the bank."

"Great point, Rick," Mike said from his perch on the windowsill. "Tim, I know from our past conversations you consider Stan one of your best trainers. He's patient, consistent, and overly generous when it comes to giving credit, right?"

"Absolutely. I'd say a year with Stan is like getting a Wharton MBA. I'm not ashamed to say even I've learned a lot from him," Tim said as he looked at each board member as if calling for a vote.

"OK, Tim, here's my call," Mike said as he vaulted off the sill. "Seth should get the job but only after you sit him down for a long talk. You need to make sure he understands all we've said here today. He particularly needs to understand that, as your son, he must not only meet the standards of his position but far exceed them. He'll need to understand that working in the family business is the hardest job there is, because if he succeeds it will be because he's your son and if he fails it will be because he was unqualified but got the job because he's your son. If he still wants to work for you knowing how tough it will be, bring him on. We all agree?"

Joe and Rick both nodded their assent. Now it was Tim's turn to stand up. Raising his arms as if to signal a touchdown, he said, "Gentlemen, thank you so much for your insights. I really didn't know how to respond to Seth's request in a way that was both unbiased and unemotional. After hearing all your comments I know just how to handle it, and you're right, Mike—if he wants to come aboard knowing all the additional pressures of working for his dad then he deserves a shot."

"He'll knock it out of the park, Tim," said Mike. "Now, get the waitress in here so we can order lunch before we go to the next agenda item. All this heavy thinking and raw emotion has me famished."

Chapter Eight

RAGS TO RICHES TO RAGS

(One Year Later)

"Seems like ages since we've had one of our Friday night sessions," Mike said to Tim, smiling broadly as he produced two Diamond Crown Churchills to celebrate the occasion.

"Thanks, Mike, love those cigars. In fact I just bought a box for myself and one for each member of the board. You'll get yours at the meeting next week."

"At $300 a throw, that's a heck of a gift, Tim," Mike said, a look of mild concern crossing his face.

"Well, you guys are a heck of a board, so it's a perfect match." With that Tim poured two glasses from the bottle of Jordan cabernet he had opened earlier.

"Breaking out the good stuff; you're spoiling me, Tim. I remember when we'd be sharing Two Buck Chuck and a couple of White Owls. Are we celebrating anything special?"

"I'd say so," Tim said with a big smile.

"So, what gives?"

"Well, Mike, I've got some bad news and what I hope you'll consider good news."

"Give me the bad news first."

"Well, this will likely be our last night on this patio."

"You've found a new friend?"

"No, we're moving."

"That's great, Tim. I know you've always wanted a bigger place with enough yard for a pool."

Tim could see in Mike's expression that he was unhappy with the thought of losing the Turners as neighbors.

"OK, so what's the good news? Are you putting in an in-law's suite in the basement for Marcia and me?"

"Even better—we bought the Millers' house on the other side of yours. That's the good news. I hope you agree."

"Tim, that's wonderful. I know we had a few discussions about the house last month. I thought it was out of your price range."

"We sold our place for more than we thought and the Millers dropped their price just enough for the bank to get comfortable with the deal."

"Tim, that's just fantastic. That's a great old place—great view, nice backyard, the whole package. I haven't been inside in years. How's it look?"

"In a word, dated. Definitely needs a new kitchen and baths for a start. The Millers haven't put much money into the house over the past fifteen or twenty years."

"I tell you what, Tim, I'll match your bottle of Jordan with a Dom Perignon toast when we christen your new place. Does Marcia know?"

"Yes, she and Sue are already plotting a redecorating program. I wanted to tell you myself. I hope you don't mind we kept it a secret."

"No, it's a great surprise." Although Mike was being honest, he also had a small nagging feeling that Tim was getting a little ahead of his skis. Tim and Sue had recently treated themselves to two new Audis—an A7 for him and an A5 convertible for her. Although Tim's 1040 might show him making more than $1 million, Mike knew that Tim's cash flow after paying his taxes, RCA's purchase price, and the principal payments on the company's long-term debt was less than half of that. Even if the Millers had dropped the price significantly, Tim had likely paid well over $1.2 million for the house, and the kitchen and bath remodeling, Mike knew from experience, could easily top $200,000.

The next week Mike spotted Tim walking the grounds of his new home and wigwagged him over to the fence line. Tim was talking on his cell phone and carrying a set of rolled-up blueprints. He ended his conversation just as he reached the fence. "The pool contractor is running late; he said he scheduled too many appointments today. The economy must be getting better."

"Putting the pool in right away, then?"

"Yeah, if they can start digging now we can be swimming by Memorial Day. That's the goal, anyway."

"Are those the plans for the kitchen and baths?" Mike asked, pointing to Tim's rolled-up papers.

"No, these are the plans for the greenhouse we're building off the kitchen. Always wanted one. I think it will be an effective way to take me away, if only momentarily, from Cincinnati's bleak winters."

"I hope that doesn't mean you won't visit us in Florida anymore."

"Just a poor-man's substitute for a winter home, Mike. Believe me, I'll come as often as you invite me."

"You sure have a lot going on. Are you going to try to get all the interior work done before you move in?"

"That's the plan. Only glitch would be the bank not going along with the plan. They've been compliant so far."

"That's good," Mike said with little enthusiasm.

"I e-mailed last month's numbers to you today. You'll have plenty of time to do your usual analysis before the board meeting next month."

The next morning Mike worked from home spreading RCA's numbers. His thorough review, which he hadn't done for a couple of months, included a detailed analysis of RCA's trends and key performance indicators. He was massaging his temples when Marcia walked into his study and poured him his second and last cup of coffee. Any more and Marcia said he became unhinged.

"What's wrong, Mike? You look concerned."

"I'm mad at myself. I just didn't see this coming."

"What's that?"

"Tim developed a case of RAGS: Recently Acquired Growth Stagnation."

"Sounds serious," Marcia replied.

"It can be."

"So what are the symptoms?" she asked, playing along with Mike's business illness analogy.

"First, Tim's margins are eroding on almost all his business lines."

"What usually causes that?"

"Sometimes in the effort to maintain high cash flow, sales growth is being over-pursued. Prices are being cut instead of truly selling, and as a result, margins shrink. Oddly enough, this does not necessarily results in sales growth. In fact, Tim's sales curve is flat."

"Same old story, right?" said Marcia. "While love is a drug, cash is even more addictive. So is the lack of sales Tim's fault?"

"Maybe not directly, but sales management, marketing, and product development is high-level stuff. Small companies like Tim's need the founder's input and focus. Unfortunately, seems like Tim's more focused on conspicuous consumption. I'm also seeing a lack of focus on controlling selling, general, and administrative expenses. It's really counterintuitive—you'd think with the over-pursuit of cash flow, the company would be somewhat focused on cost cutting. But, once again, cost cutting requires high-level input, and Tim doesn't really have a lieutenant he can put in charge of an effort like that. It's up to him and he's just not focused."

"I know it's kind of disappointing, but it seems to me that you, or should I say we, went through a period back when you still owned See and Be Seen when we were living a bit above our means."

"Yeah, I recall my banker figuratively grabbing me by the scruff of the neck and informing me the bank's love was conditional. Although he didn't directly threaten to kick me out, he did point out I seemed to be more focused on taking money out of the company rather than what needed to be put in, namely my time and undivided attention. I was young and impressionable enough to take his advice very seriously, if I recall."

"I remember you coming home that evening with your entrepreneurial tail between your legs. I think you canceled your order for a new Porsche."

"Yeah, that hurt. But, as my mother used to say, I lived."

"So are you going to call Tim on the carpet before your board meeting?" asked Marcia.

"I'm e-mailing him this afternoon to tell him that we need to talk and ask him to stop by here before work tomorrow. This may get a little rough, so I don't want to be somewhere where we could be overheard."

Tim reviewed Mike's e-mail and could tell by the tone and the request to meet at his house at seven thirty the following morning that he had something serious on his mind.

Promptly at seven thirty the next morning Tim nervously knocked on Mike's door. Mike welcomed him and he followed Mike to his study.

"Tim, in preparation for our meeting, I pulled out your Devine Inventory personality test."

"I remember taking that. Didn't all the board members take it too?"

"We did. Maybe you recall you scored exceptionally high in leadership and problem solving but fairly low in strategic thinking."

"Yeah, I recall you saying I needed to be a good problem solver because I failed to plan," Tim said with a wry grin.

"So do you think there's some truth to that, Tim?"

"No question, I definitely need some help creating and executing a plan. I'm more of a read-and-react kind of guy."

"Good for Navy SEALs, not so good for CEO's. Wouldn't you agree?"

"You're right. So what are you getting at, Mike?"

"Tim, I truly believe you were born to run a business. I just don't think you were born to manage one. Unfortunately your numbers seem to support me. Look," he continued. "I'm seeing clear signs of what I call RAGS." Tim looked at Mike quizzically, but let him continue. "Recently Acquired Growth Stagnation. This condition is usually contracted when two contagions combine. Number one, the owner's lifestyle is vacuuming all the cash out of the business and as a result the business is infected with the second contagion—that is, it doesn't have the cash necessary to hire effective middle management, which it sorely needs. No cash and inadequate management is a lethal combination. However, I think we've caught it early enough, but you need to take some corrective measures fast."

"This isn't just about our new house, is it?"

"No, it's not just that. You have to admit you've been a bit caught up in consumption: the new cars, the house, pool, and greenhouse. Those are all significant non-appreciating assets."

"Mike, I've heard you say it a million times: You've got to have some fun, so reward yourself."

"Yes, but not at the expense of the business. Look, Tim, like so many entrepreneurs, you had a pretty modest upbringing, you're competitive, and you therefore have the need to show that you're successful. Nothing wrong with that—in fact it's a strong motivation—however, it can also cloud business judgment. When your passion shifts from your business, the source of your income, to spending your business's income, you begin to lose focus. Hey, look, this is pretty common. Many, if not most entrepreneurs overspend on conspicuous consumption like life is one long high school reunion. That doesn't mean it's right."

"Mike, I think you might be overreacting to a couple of flat quarters. The bank still loves us."

"Please don't get defensive. I know you're still in compliance with your bank covenants—I checked—but as you know, your interest rate increases as your fixed charge coverage ratio declines, and it is declining, so your cost of capital is increasing."

"You're right about our interest rate, but I guess I don't see the company's current performance as quite the problem you do."

"I know you don't. What I'm telling you is you need to see it for what it is, an indication that you need to make some changes. We'll meet again before the board meeting, after you've had a chance to reflect on our discussion."

Later that morning Tim, still stinging from Mike's harsh words, examined his conscience and the spreadsheets Mike had prepared, and concluded that Mike was right. Tim's passion had shifted from growing his company to consuming its profits. Furthermore, he had allowed his family's newly outsize "needs" to determine what he took from the business rather than taking only what was left after the business's growth capital was covered. Tim also had to admit that he had shirked one of his primary duties: sales. Although he knew he was the company's best salesperson, he had tried unsuccessfully, as Mike's spreadsheet indicated, to delegate that task. As much as he hated to face it, the company's performance was entirely his fault. Tim was ashamed.

A few days later Mike arranged to meet at Tim's office. He hoped yielding home field advantage to Tim would make their meeting more conversational and less confrontational.

Mike sat in a club chair directly across from Tim's Stickley desk. "Your office is really nice, Tim—authoritative but homey."

"So now you're going to play nice, Mike? Doesn't really suit you," Tim said somewhat seriously.

"I know I was a little rough on you, but I've been through all of this myself, so I know RAGS left undiagnosed can kill a business. If I've learned anything about running a business it's that it requires constant vigilance and plenty of capital. RAGS deprives it of both."

"I suppose the reason I took it so hard is that I know you're one hundred percent correct, and frankly I'm embarrassed."

"Understandable, but the real question is whether you're ready to put your helmet back on and get in the game. Are you?"

"Absolutely. I'm formulating a game plan right now. I'll complete it by the board meeting."

"Tim, I hope you know that the cure is not an event but a commitment to a process. And the process needs to address the essence of operating a business."

Tim, now a bit confused, replied, "Not sure I follow. Isn't the essence of business making money?"

"Obviously making money is important, but the essence of the smart operation of a business is long-term value creation. I'm sure you remember our discussion about you reaching exit velocity to leave your job."

"Yeah, you hit that nail on the head. My frustration definitely propelled me out of the hospital into entrepreneurship."

"Tim, a truly successful business creates a different kind of exit velocity. When done right, a business, either through its eventual sale at a high price or through a consistently growing bottom line, creates financial exit velocity, freedom from financial worry. However, when a business is being run primarily for cash flow, it is just a lifestyle business."

"I've heard that term, *lifestyle business.* I suppose that's because the business is run either to meet the level of cash flow necessary to fund the owner's lifestyle, or the owner's lifestyle is just high enough to use all the cash flow."

"Exactly. I'm sure that you can see your business as headed in that direction, right?"

Tim, shaking his head sheepishly, said, "No question."

"Tim, the long-term effect of operating a lifestyle business is disastrous. The culture can quickly change from go-go to no-go. And if the condition persists, it can be difficult to turn the culture around and prospects for growth are significantly diminished. It's the same old story. Either you're growing or you're dying. When the owner is vacuuming out all the cash the balance sheet is weak because there is too much debt, and as a result new capital, if it's available at all, is expensive."

"I can see the pattern," Tim said. "I can also see that I need to commit more of my time to the company, particularly in sales and the development of the younger folks. I know it's up to me to develop the next generation of change makers."

"Now you're talking. As we've discussed a million times, a

company's value is predicated on the amount and predictability of future cash flows. No way to do this without spending the time and money necessary to develop the people and processes that make that happen, and these processes can't be dependent on you. The best, most valuable businesses can run on remote control. If a business doesn't need the owner to operate successfully, unlike RCA when you bought it, you can legitimately add back the owner's salary to determine adjusted EBITDA. A lofty but attainable goal."

"It all sounds so logical. It's hard to believe I couldn't see this myself."

"Just too close to it, Tim. No need for self-flagellation, just self control," Mike said with his most benign smile.

"I guess so, but it's still embarrassing."

"I've seen it many times. I'd say most of my acquisitions were from RAGS victims. Got the businesses at a discount and turned them around fast. I was always surprised to see business owners fall prey to their own outsize need for cash, which in turn made them both unwilling and unable to take the new risks needed to continue profitable growth. You know, Tim, it's really a paradox."

"How's that?" Tim asked, now seeing this discussion as less a guilt trip and more like one of Mike's critical business/life lessons.

"Think about it—the owner's new aversion to risk actually creates more risk for his business, which leads to reduced value."

"Dangerous cycle."

"No question. Businesses, no matter how much cash they're producing, must constantly replenish human and intellectual capital. The most successful businesses are constantly reinventing themselves—think Apple. This is a hyperactive process the owner must lead.

"Tim, I hope you don't mind—I've shared my spreadsheet and my thoughts with the rest of the board."

"Not at all. I have two weeks to prepare my curative plan. It'll be complete for the meeting."

The board was assembled in its usual room at the Queen City Club. Tim called the meeting to order and after dispensing with the formalities said, "I decided to depart from our usual process and be the only presenter from RCA. I promise to be concise. I've put together my reengagement plan, which, as you can see from our agenda, is our only topic for today."

"We're ready to be wowed," Rick said in his typical good-natured manner.

Joe chimed in, "Mike gave a little flavor of your discussions leading up to the meeting. Sounds like he roughed you up a little, Tim."

"Honestly, I think the punishment fit the crime," Tim said, maintaining a steadfast gaze at Joe, indicating the seriousness with which he took Mike's critique.

Tim began, "I have strictly scheduled a significant amount of my time in the office. I'm hoping being tightly scheduled will not only prevent me from dreaming up new ways to spend money but will also allow me to spend enough time with my management team for them to be properly informed and, I hope, intensely focused.

"I'm also scheduling at least two trips per month to visit our largest clients. I know from previous experience this always leads to new business."

Nodding his head, Rick said, "In the old days it seemed like every time I turned around you were in my office proposing some new service. You consistently presented a compelling case."

"Thanks, Rick. I hope I haven't lost the magic."

"OK, Tim, what's next? This is getting fun," Mike said, rubbing his hands together.

"I've decided it's time for me to hire a COO. Mike, you were right, I'm not a good manager. I need somebody to make sure the trains run on time, so I can spend more time with clients and on more high-value initiatives, like new business lines."

Mike stood up and while applauding exclaimed, "Bravo, Tim! I know that will be expensive, but like most expensive things, it will be worth it. Looks like you took our discussions to heart."

"I did, Mike. I realized you were right and so was my Devine Inventory: I'm not a planner; I'm a creative doer, so I definitely need to hire a planner." Tim continued, "The next item is more personal, but after my discussions with Mike, I thought it was appropriate for our board meeting." The board members looked at each other and Tim with a bit of skepticism.

"I've put my family on a budget, and Mike, you'll be happy to know I've shelved the greenhouse project. However, the hole's dug for the pool, so that's going ahead as planned."

Joe, doing his best Dutch uncle, said, "Wise choice, Tim. I know it feels like you've got a mile-long want list and inadequate time to fill it, but take it from someone much older and with a highly consumptive lifestyle for an accountant—a lot of your wants either expire with time or at least change significantly. Not to mention you'll learn you get almost as much, if not more satisfaction from planning as you do from doing. And you'll also find that proper planning ensures the appropriate time between projects." Both Mike and Rick let out knowing chuckles, indicating their assent.

"Lastly," Tim continued, "through my recent spate of reconnecting phone calls with clients, I've found an acquisition I think makes sense. It is just the right size for us: sales of $5 million and $600,000 of EBITDA. I am in the process of preparing an LOI and would like some input. I think it will take about $3 million to get the deal done. I feel so strongly about the deal that I've told the bank I would put $250,000 of my own money back in if they agree to drop the rate on the acquisition financing a point, and they agreed."

Mike said, "Impressive show of confidence, Tim."

"Thanks, Mike. I got to thinking that investing in my business now is far less risky than it was when I started it, so why not double down?"

As Mike and Tim were leaving the meeting Mike put his arm around Tim's shoulder and said, "That's the most insightful self-analysis I've ever witnessed, Tim. It was equal parts tent revival and Harvard Business School Management 501."

Tim told Mike, "I went back to your ten entrepreneurial questions and replayed many of our discussions and found I knew just what to do."

"Tim, during your presentation today I had a revelation that I need to add an eleventh question, and I think it may deserve top billing."

"What's that—'Can you stop spending like a drunken sailor?'"

"Hardly. I think the number one question entrepreneurs need to ask themselves is whether they are willing to truly examine their conscience, find their faults, and muster the courage to correct them."

"I guess I should be proud I've been able to add to your list," Tim said with a bit of sarcasm.

"No, really, Tim, you should be proud that you're open to constructive criticism. Your presentation today proved to me you've got what it takes to take RCA to the next level."

"Thanks, Mike. That means a lot coming from you."

"You've got plenty of hard work ahead of you. As you and I have discussed often, even though your long-term plan may not be to sell RCA, you should always operate it as though that was your goal. If you can create and execute a plan that proves RCA can produce consistent growth and consistently higher profits, you'll have created real value. By now you realize that should be the number one goal of operating your own business."

"I know that, but make sure I don't ever lose sight of it again."

"Don't worry, I will," Mike said as he led Tim into the bar on the first floor of the Queen City Club. "Now, let me buy you a beer and I'll tell you about my next deal. I just might need a partner with some very specific skills and good judgment, and I think I know just the guy."

Chapter Nine

IN SUM

The next morning Tim smiled as he replayed his discussion with Mike at the Queen City Club bar. Knowing Mike's strong feelings about avoiding partnerships, he was flattered that Mike believed he would bring significant value to his latest venture, a home health care equipment company. According to Mike, Tim's deep understanding of the medical reimbursement system would be essential to the profitable growth of TechMed. As Mike put it, Tim passed the acid test for partners; that is, he had skills that couldn't be acquired for cash alone. Thinking about all he had learned running RCA over the past years, he had to admit, perhaps immodestly, that he had learned a lot about both how and how not to operate an entrepreneurial business, and he had the scar tissue to prove it. Just as he was getting lost in his own thoughts about his business journey, his phone buzzed.

"Tim, it's Sue," said his assistant.

"Thanks, Meggie, put her through."

"You seem to time your calls perfectly," Tim said to Sue. "I was just sitting here feeling proud of myself because Mike invited me to partner with him on TechMed. Fun, but wholly unproductive."

"That's OK—you're permitted to pat yourself on the back every once in a while."

"You're right, as the boss, no one else is likely to do it."

"Not their job. I'd say you're driven enough; you don't need adoring throngs."

"Agreed—they'd only get in the way throwing rose petals and all. What's up?"

"Well, your self-congratulatory reverie is well timed. I got a call from my sister Jayne. Her brother-in-law, Dave, is considering leaving Procter and Gamble and acquiring a business—some sort of juice distributorship—and would like to pick your brain."

"Surprising—I thought Dave was on a fast track to becoming a brand manager."

"He is, but P and G wants him to relocate to France. With two high-schoolers, it's just not the right time, I guess."

"That would be a tough call. I'm not sure I agree with it, but I'd be happy to talk to him."

Since Sue had thoughtfully sent Tim Dave's contact information as they were talking, Tim decided he'd send Dave an e-mail before they met. Remembering how he was caught a bit flat- footed, not only during that first lunch with Mike at Aglamesis Brothers but also at several of their subsequent sessions, he decided to hit Dave with Entrepreneurship 101 through 601. Although a both-barrel blast might be intimidating to most would-be entrepreneurs, he believed Dave, a Wharton MBA, would be receptive. Moreover, despite Dave's first-class education and his fifteen years with a multinational, Tim knew his understanding of what it would be like operating his own business with his own capital at risk was dangerously lacking.

Tim buzzed Meggie and asked her to hold his calls for the next hour. He got up, closed his office door, and began typing:

Dave,

Sue told me about your opportunity with the juice distributorship. It sounds interesting. I know from my search for a company several years ago, distributorships and light manufacturers are the types of businesses most new entrepreneurs seek. Unfortunately, that will indicate higher demand, so be prepared to pay top dollar. Although that tidbit is likely a bit of a BRO (blinding revelation of the obvious), what follows will be anything but.

Before I purchased RCA, I had a long lunch with Mike Collins, a lawyer/CPA/entrepreneur and my mentor. Over cheeseburgers and milk shakes, as I recall, Mike outlined ten questions potential entrepreneurs must ask themselves. After I left that meeting I wrote down all ten. I have referred to them so often as I've encountered the inevitable obstacles of operating a business that I can list them without opening my middle drawer, the only contents of which is a laminated sheet with my original handwritten notes on these all-important ten questions. In order to spare you the daunting exercise of deciphering my handwriting, I won't scan my original sheet. My thoughts, which I added to Mike's list right after our meeting, and which mostly question the list's accuracy, are now embarrassing and unworthy of your review. By now I'm sure you are practically breathless, so . . . the ten questions:

1) Can you live with the uncertainty associated with running your own business? I know your highly successful career at Procter & Gamble was not a foregone conclusion. However, even a moderately successful career at P&G results in a comfortable retirement. This is anything but assured when you're operating your own business. Many factors completely outside your control can and will affect your business. Living with that uncertainty is a price you pay for a potentially bigger future.

2) How would you rate your tolerance for risk? Probably another BRO, but the only way to grow your business and make more money is to assume more risk. I know from some painful experiences that this includes not only what you invest up front but also, to use a betting analogy, doubling down later by reinvesting your company's profits. Sounds easy now, but believe me, being successful has its own set of self-control issues. (More on that later.) In addition to financial risk, you also need to risk a significant amount of your time and talent. No matter how broad your bandwidth, you'll find the work-life balance a challenge.

3) What's your relationship with your money? This may be a tough one since your position at P&G has been your principal source of income and your investment income is likely a distant second. When you own your own business, your principal source of income is also your largest investment. In addition, since you're going to be required to personally guarantee, at least initially, all corporate debt, you're essentially laying your entire net worth on the line every day. The firewall that currently exists between your job and your investments vanishes. You really need to believe in your own skills and judgment. It's scary, but you'll learn to love it.

4) Can you lead people? Since your distributorship will have employees of every stripe, being able to lead not only management personnel, which you're used to, but also the rank and file, is critical. All of your employees need to realize you care about them as people. It's hard to expect your truck drivers (one of your company's principal sales contacts) to be thinking of ways to improve the company's performance while on their routes if they don't believe you're doing your part to improve their lives. You'll find that output will increase exponentially if your company has a paternalistic quality. If you want to achieve your dream, you need to help your employees achieve theirs!

5) Are you competitive? I suppose this may seem like an unnecessary question based on the requisite mentality set forth under number two, particularly since the willingness to take risk is usually accompanied by a high degree of competitiveness, but you'll find it's more than that. You must not only want to beat your competition, but, as Mike put it to me, you need to have the burning desire to provide services and products that are so good your clients are raving fans and your competition finds you unbeatable.

6) What's your work ethic? I know Procter's had you moving all over the U.S. and that you were a top-flight student, but owning your own business is a highly consumptive relationship. You will end up being the toughest boss you've ever had, by far. The only difference is now it will seem like fun.

7) Are you a good listener? Listening to your company's customers must be a passion. While IQ may be particularly valuable inside a large company, EQ, or emotional quotient, becomes more important when you're dealing with customers, and even more so with employees. All that you've ever heard about active listening must be brought to bear. Even more important, you'll need to solicit and listen to your professionals' advice. I know getting answers to legal and accounting questions is relatively easy inside a big multinational, and it's free. As a business owner you'll be in constant contact with your lawyer and even more so with your accountant. I found that the business wisdom I've gained from my professional relationships, particularly with Paul Griffin, my CPA, is among the most valuable of my business assets.

I know the advice will seem expensive at the beginning; however, after you've avoided a couple of big mistakes, you'll characterize the advice as valuable rather than expensive.

8) Can you sell? I know that P&G is one of the world's largest advertisers, and I know advertising is not selling, but I also know that the competitive game of getting shelf space in retailers requires strong selling techniques. You'll need those techniques, since, as you know, the best businesses are not those with the cheapest products, but those whose customers believe they are receiving the best value. Selling based on value takes talent and vigilance.

9) Do you have a skill that adds real value to your new business? As Mike put it, you need to be the best player at one position or the second-best player at several positions. Since you had years of hands-on experience working on Citrus Hill, back when P&G was in the juice business, you should have this one covered. Based on the previous question, I'm sure you can see how difficult it would be to add real value to your business if all you could do was help administer the business. I supposed I'm one of the rare exceptions—a CPA who made the transition to entrepreneur—but then again, I knew plenty about revenue cycle management before I bought RCA.

10) Do you have a financial goal for your business? You might be tempted to say, "Yes, to make lots of money," and although that's part of it, I've learned it's only part. Even more critical is to operate your business so that it becomes a transferable asset. So even if you plan on passing the business on to your children rather than selling it, you should be constantly evaluating whether your decisions are not just resulting in more profits but are also creating more long-term value. It's easy to get caught up in the pursuit of short-term profits and forget that real value comes from sustainability, which often comes at the price of reduced current earnings. Since big companies, like P&G, are constantly making decisions based on long-term goals, you might find it hard to believe, but most entrepreneurs learn to think long term only after a major setback or two.

Before I step down from the soapbox, I feel compelled to share a few of my most critical decision points with the hope of helping you avoid the big mistake. Believe me, the opportunities to make the big mistake lurk in what will look initially like the most innocuous situations, like a friend or employee wanting to partner with you in your new venture. Very early on I had a key employee ask to buy in. She only wanted twenty-five percent of the company and was willing to pay a fair price based upon the company's value at the time. After a lengthy discussion with Mike, and later with Paul, I was able to satisfy her with a deferred compensa-

tion plan linked to the growth of RCA's value. The difference between the cost of that plan and the value of twenty-five percent of RCA today is over $1 million. Enough said.

I know you've got two high-school-age children and one in grade school, so you're a ways from this decision, but you're likely to have one or more of your children want to join your business. I'm afraid that this is particularly true now, since the economy is not providing great entry-level positions. As you may know, Seth joined me a year ago, and it's worked out great, partly because he had a great academic background and some valuable experience with the bank, but mostly because he took a keen interest in the business right from the beginning. Realizing this, I used him as a junior sounding board. This gave Seth a considerable head start on developing his critical-thinking skills. If you get the sense that any of your children are interested in joining you, and for the right reasons, I'd promote this interest by sharing some of your business issues with them. You could end up with not only a great addition to your management team like I have, but also a built-in exit strategy.

Lastly, be aware that as intoxicating as making your own money can be, spending it can be a truly dangerous addiction. Unlike your current situation, where your long-term salary expectations have nothing to do with how you save or invest, the converse is true when you own your own business. Your future salary as well as the company's future profits are

directly linked to your willingness to reinvest in your busi-
ness. This includes not just your money, but more important,
your time and attention. It may be hard to imagine that you
could lose sight of this, but believe me, it's more the rule than
the exception.

Dave, I'm sorry, this is probably too much information, but
someday you'll thank me; I promise. Being your own boss
and the boss of many others is scary, because in the end it's all
up to you, but that's exactly why it's so rewarding.

Good Luck,
Tim

Tim sent the e-mail to Dave and immediately began typing an
e-mail to Mike.

Mike,
Thanks for the opportunity to partner with you on TechMed.
I know we'll work well together (we already do) and that
I'll add value in a way that only a partner can. I'm also sure
there's a bumpy road ahead, but challenges are what make it
fun. Looking forward to the ride!

Tim

Appendix A

REPORT

Tim, as promised, using the information RCA provided, we reconciled the seller's discretionary cash flow (SDCF) set forth in the offering book to the more standard adjusted EBITDA valuation metric. Our analysis indicates that the sellers added back several items to net income, as reported on a generally accepted accounting principal (GAAP) basis, to arrive at SDCF. These items include interest, taxes, depreciation, and all salary paid to Pete, plus his country club dues, car expenses, and his nonbusiness travel expenses. Obviously Pete believes the cash flow after these add-backs would be available to the buyer to pay himself and any debt incurred to buy the company, and provide a return on the cash invested.

With that as our starting point, we made several adjustments to arrive at what we believe to be the appropriate adjusted EBITDA number.

The first adjustment was to deduct a fair level of compensation to be paid to you to run the business. We used a local employee database of health-care-related companies to determine a figure for the various levels of sales. We also deducted the appropriate retirement plan contributions and health insurance.

RCA leases its office space from a building Pete owns. Our analysis indicates the rent paid by RCA is $20,000 above market. Since you could save this $20,000 on your rent, we added it back each year.

The company tried to expand its footprint in Detroit by leasing space near Detroit hospitals during 2007 and 2008. Since this office has been closed, we added back the cost of operating it for those years.

Our last adjustment is to deduct the cost of engaging a board of advisers. Although a company RCA's size would not normally have a board, our extensive experience with health-care-related businesses suggests that having other health care specialists and hospital administrators as advisers is practically mandatory to ensure a company like RCA stays ahead of the curve. This is especially true with the ever-changing world of medical reimbursement in which RCA operates.

We also analyzed the assets you'll be buying and the liabilities you'll be assuming. As you can see from the balance sheet presented there are only a few differences between RCA's existing assets and liabilities and those that will come across in the transaction.

Customarily sellers keep any cash in the company, so we subtracted the $100,000 in cash currently on the company's books.

Since you've informed us you're not going to take over RCA's lease, we removed the value of the leasehold improvements. We also reduced the value of the furniture and equipment by $20,000, to bring it in line with our opinion of its fair market value.

The "at closing" balance sheet shows that, as a result of these reductions, you'll be buying tangible assets of $1,302,000 and assuming liabilities of $735,000, yielding net tangible equity purchased of $567,000.

I passed on this information to Doug Edwards. His report follows.

Paul

Appendix B

Tim,

As you would expect, our valuation databases, which contain the size and prices of companies sold, don't include many transactions as small as the RCA deal. However, larger transactions in the health care area have given us a good feel for the current market values of larger companies. From that information and my estimate of the additional risk associated with a smaller company, I was able to arrive at an appropriate multiple for your deal. I was also able to somewhat confirm this through "telephone research" with a good friend, Kent Smith. Kent is a partner at a private equity firm in Cleveland that bought a fairly large health care consulting firm earlier this year.

There were a few transactions in which strategic buyers (those already in the heath care arena) paid higher-than-market multiples for companies, likely because of synergies or because the target company filled some perceived gap in the buyer's service offering. However, the data showed a convergence around multiples between 7 and 9.5 for larger deals. As you know, smaller deals like yours are riskier, which reduces the multiples buyers are willing to pay. Based upon RCA's size, which was much smaller than the Cleveland deal and any of the deals in our database (in fact, the smallest deal was a company with $20 million in sales), I believe the appropriate multiple is between 6.5 and 7.5. Our most specific intelligence—that is, the company Kent's firm purchased—was $25 million in sales with EBITDA of $3.5 million, and he said they paid right at eight times. In sum, I'd say an offer at the low end, or 6.5, can be justified based upon RCA's size.

The obvious next question is which EBITDA figure this multiple should be applied to. I am sure you have seen various techniques, such as averaging the five-year EBITDA figures or using a weighted average whereby the most current EBITDA is weighted most heavily. In my opinion, those techniques are inappropriate because RCA's EBITDA shows a strong upward trend. When analyzing value, the likely EBITDA next year and beyond is the most important figure to determine. In RCA's case, I believe the most recent year's EBITDA is most predictive of future years' EBITDA.

Applying the 6.5 multiple to the most recent year's EBITDA yields a value of approximately $1,872,000. This figure represents enterprise value, which assumes a balance sheet with no long-term debt and with average working capital (as you know, working capital is current assets less current liabilities). Since RCA's long-term debt is low and their working capital is high, an upward adjustment in value is called for.

The working capital indicated on the "at closing" balance sheet is approximately $600,000 (current assets of $1,252,000 less current liabilities of $685,000), which represents a current ratio of 2:1 (1,252,000 divided by 685,000). The industry average is 1.1:1. Applying this ratio to the current liabilities indicates the company should operate on approximately $750,000 in working capital (685,000 x 1.1). Subtracting this figure from the $1,252,000, the value of the current assets, yields excess working capital of approximately $500,000, which, added to the enterprise value of $1,872,000, indicates a total value of $2,372,000 for RCA.

Tim, I know this is a lot of information to assimilate; however, I know you have a strong financial background and a great sounding board in Mike Collins. So you're likely up to the task. Even so, feel free to call with questions.

Doug

	2006	2007	2008	2009	2010
Income	$2,500,000	$3,200,000	$4,000,000	$4,600,000	$5,000,000
Cost of Sales	<1,500,000>	<1,760,000>	<2,120,000>	<2,530,000>	<2,800,000>
SG&A	<800,000>	<1,140,000>	<1,460,000>	<1,590,000>	<1,600,000>
SDCF ᴬ	200,000	300,000	420,000	480,000	600,000
Officers' Comp ᴮ	<120,000>	<150,000>	<200,000>	<220,000>	<250,000>
Retirement Plan ᴮ	<10,000>	<12,000>	<20,000>	<25,000>	<30,000>
Health Ins ᴮ	<12,000>	<12,000>	<12,000>	<12,000>	<12,000>
Rent ᶜ	20,000	20,000	20,000	20,000	20,000
Michigan Office ᴰ		40,000	60,000		
Boa Fees ᴱ	<40,000>	<40,000>	<40,000>	<40,000>	<40,000>
EBITDA	$38,000	$146,000	$228,000	$203,000	$288,000

Footnotes:

A. SDCF was originally calculated by adding the following items back to GAAP basis net income: interest, taxes, depreciation, and all officer-related compensation and perquisites, including car, country club dues, and "personal" travel.

The following items (B through D) were needed, in our opinion, to accurately state adjusted EBITDA, which could be used for comparison to valuation database figures.

B. Officer-related compensation, retirement plan contribution, and health insurance are all per local employer resource data for CEOs of companies of similar size to RCA.

C. The company rents its office space from an entity controlled by the business owner. Our analysis indicates the rent exceeds market by $20,000 per year.

D. The company incurred nonrecurring costs in 2007 and 2008 when it set up a branch office in Detroit, Michigan. The office was closed in November 2008.

E. In our opinion, a company of this size in the health care consulting industry would generally engage a board of outside advisers. This would include at least three independent members. The figure represents the cost of four meetings per year.

Appendix C

H.F. Holdings, LLC
100 William Howard Taft Road
Cincinnati, OH 45206

October 5, 2011

Mr. Peter M. Grove
RCA LLC
200 Eden Park Drive
Cincinnati, OH 45206

Dear Mr. Grove:

This letter sets forth our preliminary understandings and intentions ("Letter of Intent") with respect to an acquisition by H.F. Holdings, LLC ("Buyer") of certain assets including: all current lines of business; certain operating assets, including certain accounts receivable but not including cash (the "Assets") of RCA LLC (the "Company") on the terms and conditions set forth herein. Except for the provisions of Sections 4 through 8 hereof, inclusive, and this introductory paragraph, this Letter of Intent is nonbinding and contains proposed points that may or may not become part of eventual definitive agreements. Thus, this Letter of Intent is not an offer to purchase the Assets of the Company, but is instead merely an expression of the present intentions and interests of the Buyer and the Company with respect to the proposed transaction.

1. The purchase price proposed to be paid by Buyer to Company for the purchase of the Assets of the Company would be $2,450,000, payable as follows, and is based on net working capital at closing of $570,000:

a. Cash at closing in the amount of $1,275,000

b. Assumption of $685,000 in liabilities

c. Note from the Buyer in the principal amount of $490,000

2. Other conditions to Buyer's obligation to close the transaction would include:

a. Execution by certain key employees of a three-year Employment and Non-Competition Agreement with Buyer or the Company, which will include standard terms and conditions including termination provisions and post-termination clauses for Non-Competition.

b. If necessary, the assignment and transfer of all contracts with third parties and all Employment and Non-Competition Agreements between the Company and its sales staff. The Company would also represent in the definitive agreement that the Company is not aware of any sales associate of the Company that is currently not a party to such an agreement.

c. The transfer of appropriate equipment leases.

d. Satisfactory completion of due diligence on the financial condition, operations, and business of the Company; the receipt of any necessary third-party consents, employee information, customer lists and overviews, and other customary closing conditions. Further, Company would represent and warrant that the Company's assets are free and clear of liens and encumbrances and that the financial information that has been provided to Buyer (i.e., financial statements, including income statements and balance sheets) fairly and accurately depicts the financial condition of the Company for the periods indicated.

e. Buyer obtaining financing for the acquisition and working capital on terms and conditions satisfactory to Buyer.

f. Buyer's satisfaction with all due diligence, including but not limited to contracts, environmental matters, financial statements and related matters, and employment agreements and related matters.

3. The transactions contemplated by this Letter of Intent would occur under and be governed by a definitive agreement to be negotiated and executed by the Company and Buyer (the "Purchase Agreement"). The Purchase Agreement would contain warranties, representation, noncompetition and nondisclosure covenants, conditions precedent, and indemnities, as are customary in commercial asset acquisition transactions and as mutually agreed by the Company and Buyer.

4. After execution of this Letter of Intent, during normal business hours the Company would provide to Buyer and its representatives full access to the books and records, personnel and facilities, customers, and banking institutions of the Company. During this period, the Company will operate its business in the ordinary course of business consistent with past practices.

5. Buyer and the Company hereby agree that until January 1, 2012 (or, if sooner, until such time Buyer, in its sole discretion, abandons or terminates this Letter of Intent), the Company, its agents, or its personnel shall not in any way (a) solicit, directly or indirectly, any offer to purchase any of the Assets or any of the capital stock of the Company, or any offer to enter into a merger, recapitalization, consolidation, or similar transaction; (b) enter into any discussions, negotiations, or agreements with any person or entity that contemplates or provides for any such transaction; or (c) provide to any persons or entities, other than Buyer or its representatives, any information or data relating to the proposed transaction described herein.

6. Except as and to the extent required by law, neither Buyer nor Company will disclose or use, and will direct its representatives (and in the case of the Company, direct its personnel) not to disclose or use to the detriment of the other, the Confidential Information (as

defined below) of the other furnished, or to be furnished, by Buyer or the Company, as the case may be, at any time or in any manner other than in connection with the evaluation of the transactions proposed in this Letter of Intent. For purposes of this Section 6, "Confidential Information" means any information about Buyer and/or the Company, as the case may be, unless (a) such information is publicly available or is generally known in the industry or is already known to the nondisclosing party or its representatives or to others not bound by a duty of confidentiality or such information becomes publicly available through no fault of the nondisclosing party or its representative, or (b) upon opinion of counsel, the use of such information is necessary or appropriate in connection with legal proceedings. Upon written request of the disclosing party, any Confidential Information in the other party's possession, as the case may be, shall be destroyed and such destroying party shall certify in writing that it has done so.

7. Except as and to the extent required by law, without the prior written consent of the other party, neither party will, and each will direct its representative (and in the case of the Company, its personnel) not to make, directly or indirectly, any public comment, statement, or communication with respect to, or otherwise to disclose or to permit the disclosure of the existence of discussions regarding a possible transaction between the parties or any of the terms, conditions, or other aspects of the transaction proposed in the Letter of Intent. If a party is required by law to make any such disclosure, it must first provide to the other party the content of the proposed disclosure, the reasons that such disclosure is required by law, and the time and place that the disclosure will be made.

8. This Letter of Intent shall be governed by, and construed under, the laws of the State of Ohio.

As noted above, this letter is nonbinding (except for the provisions of Sections 4 through 8, inclusive, and of the introductory paragraph), and is intended only to provide a framework for negotiations of the transactions contemplated hereby. Please acknowledge your agreement with the foregoing by signing both copies in the space provided below, and return one (1) signed original in the enclosed envelope.

Sincerely,

H.F. Holdings, LLC

By:

 Timothy C. Turner

Date:_____

Agreed to and Accepted by:

RCA LLC

By:

 Peter M. Grove

Date:_____

Patrick J. Burke

Patrick J. Burke, a CPA and attorney, is the managing partner of Burke & Schindler, CPAs, a firm he founded in 1984. Since the firm's inception, Burke has continuously recruited the most talented professionals to broaden the scope of the practice and to ensure Burke & Schindler clients receive top-notch service. The firm specializes in business consulting, taxation, audit and accounting, executive recruiting and staffing, and retirement plan administration.

Burke is a respected expert in business acquisitions and sales, deal structuring, and succession planning. In addition, he has advised more than eighty highly successful start-ups. His commitment to a proactive approach has earned him the trust and respect of his clients. He exceeds expectations by becoming clients' go-to business adviser.

Burke has been a featured lecturer on entrepreneurship at the University of Dayton and numerous seminars. He is a former member of the "Forty Under 40" business leaders in Cincinnati and a member of the Ohio Society of Certified Public Accountants, the American Institute of Certified Public Accountants, and the Ohio and American Bar Associations.

Currently, he is chairman of the board of directors of a closely held $20 million medical consulting company and a board member (including chairman of the audit and compensation committees) of a closely held $400 million real estate services business.

Burke received his J.D. from the University of Cincinnati Law School and his B.S. cum laude from the University of Dayton.

Outside of work, Burke is active with Boys Hope Girls Hope of Cincinnati, DePaul Cristo Rey High School, and The Dynamic Catholic Institute.

If you'd like help buying a business,
running the one you have more efficiently
and profitably, or selling your business for
top dollar, please contact Patrick Burke:

www.burkecpa.com
901 Adams Crossing
Cincinnati, OH 45202
513-455-8200
Business@BurkeCPA.com